Lighthouses and Mariti

TO SAFELY GUIDE THEIR WAY

by

Kenneth Sutton-Jones

Copyright © 1998

Published by
B&T Publications

PUBLISHED BY B&T PUBLICATIONS
10 Orchard Way · Highfield · Southampton
Hampshire SO17 1RD

International Standard Book Number

ISBN 1-901043-19-3

International Standard Serial Number

ISSN 1461 5029

Back cover photograph by Karl R. Spitzer

Printed by CiT Printing Services

Kenneth Sutton-Jones

AUTHOR'S PREFACE

Invention and technological development are changing the *'shape'* of Aids to Navigation at sea. My own sixty years' world-wide experience, in planning and providing the apparatus for Lighthouses, Lightvessels, Beacons and Buoys, is very small in the context of the thousands of years that man has sailed the seas.

As we approach AD 2000, we get a *'glimpse'* into the future, and this has prompted my writing this Résumé of the requirements of past centuries and the dramatic changes, now taking place on the threshold of the Millennium.

My dear wife Phyllis has indeed been exceptionally tolerant of my *'Pharological Mania'*, and the reader should be aware of the Romance of this intriguing subject which, alas, is disappearing.

During the compiling of this narrative, the assistance of Martin Boyle and his specialist publishing team, Hans-Günter Spitzer and Karl R. Spitzer, is particularly acknowledged.

3

Contents   Page

Knowledge of Early Sea-Trading • Shadows, Shapes & Stars – A Manual of Pilotage

A Bold Beginning – Open Fires on Towers   6

Influence of the Romans and their Achievements   7

Centuries of Darkness & Chaos   8

Light Out of Darkness • A Measure of Control Returns

Order Out of Chaos – Philantropists or Opportunists   9

Possibly the Finest Lighthouse in the World   10

The Tower-Rock *Station Builders*   12

Ireland's Tower-Rock Builders • Continued French Influence

Rapid Progress in Scotland   16

A Variety of Sites & Conditions   17

Great Ingenuity of Construction   18

The All Important Light   20

Improved Performance – Positive Recognition   22

Reflectors   23

Recognition   24

What were the Basic Needs for the Sailor?

Development of Clear Weather Aids to Navigation   25

Value of Intensities & Majestic Optics   27

Protection from the Elements   28

Three Cardinal Advances   30

Magnificence in Attended Lighthouses   32

Other Sources of Light • Acetylene Gas   33

The Advent & Application of Electricity   34

World-wide Conversion Programme • Semi-watched Stations   38

Buoys & Beacons   39

Fog & Rain   40

Invisible Positioning   43

Morse Code & Semaphore • Various Methods of Hyperbolic Positioning

The Full Umbrella *To Guide Their Way*   45

Estuary and Channel Marking   48

The Radar Innovation   49

Crises – Firstly Oil, then Keepership Threatened • Economic Recession   50

Shippings Revised Requirements • Unmanning Major Lightstations   51

Conserving Energy   53

The Great Panacea   54

Global Positioning   55

Refinement of the Monitoring • The Pruning Process   56

The International Forum   58

See It in a Museum • Food for Thought   59

James Walker's iron pile tower of 1850.
Reproduced with kind permission of Trinity House

Knowledge of Early Sea-Trading

Ancient peoples of civilisations such as China, traversed the seas with a means for assisting navigation, probably developed long before these methods were known to Western Nations. Our knowledge of the earliest sea-traders and their needs comes mainly from the records of the Mid-Eastern or Northern Lands.

One of the first documented details of open-sea sailing and trading, refers to 40 ships which carried cedar wood from Phoenicia (Lebanon - Syria), to Pharaoh Snefru in 2700 BC. Egyptians on the Nile traded regularly with Crete before 2500 BC which, around 1800 BC, became the first *'Sea-Empire'* .

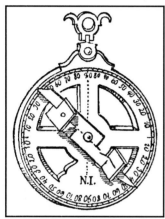

Astrolabe, introduced by Hipparchus around 150 BC. Spitzer Archive

By 1200 BC trading posts had been established in the Mediterranean and Black Sea regions, with the Phoenicians based along the North African coast, then venturing through the Straits of Gibraltar (*Calpe of the Greeks*), to obtain silver from Iberia (Spain), and tin from the Cornish mines (England).

Around 800 BC the Greeks colonised many areas along the coast of the Black Sea. They, too, sought the high quality tin from Cornwall, but by sailing a passage through the rivers of Central Europe. Navigation by astronomy was first employed around 500 BC, but although the instrument known as *'Astrolabe'* was used, its accuracy must have been dangerous and unpredictable.

Sea-trading centres were also founded by Alexander the Great in 332 BC, then followed the rise of Rome, which by 70 BC ruled the whole area.

Shadows, Shapes & Stars – A Manual of Pilotage

Meanwhile sailors became skilled in identifying the movement of stars, the profiles of islands and various coastal features, especially on clear moonlit nights.

The *'Perciplus'*, showing recognised trade routes followed by generations of sailors, together with the details of winds and currents, came into use around 400 BC. These early *'rutters'* or *'sea-charts'* described routes, landmarks, anchorages and port entrances, which, with the *'lead-line'* for assessing the depth of water, provided the first navigational aid aboard vessels.

A Bold Beginning – Open Fires on Towers

About 300 BC, a *'Bronze Statue'* was said to have been constructed by Chares, a disciple of Lysippus. It was called *'The Colossus of Rhodes'*, and appears to have stood astride the harbour, where *"Vessels passed between the legs"*. The statue was for their guidance for a period of some eighty years, before being demolished by an earthquake.

Alexandria, on the low and featureless North Egyptian coast, needed to be identifiable from the greatest possible distance. During the reign of Ptolemy Philadelphus, a friend of the Royal Family, Sostratus, designed and constructed a truly magnificent, marble-faced tower in 285 BC upon the off-lying island of

Pharos. This was some 122m (400ft) in height, which gave it a range of over 25 miles.

A wood fire was kept burning at its summit, and some believed, that the light from this was directed by a mirror. Although the superficial inscription bore the name *'Ptolemy'*, probably chiselled in a layer of soft clay by the designer; when this was eroded, the further name *'Sostratus of Cnidos'* prevailed. In 1302 the structure collapsed in an earthquake.

An impression of the ancient »Pharos« of Alexandria. Spitzer Archive

Similar *'fire-towers'* were erected by the Phoenicians and other cultures, to assist vessels in reaching a port or safe haven (*Aegean–200 BC, Turris Caepionis–100 BC and Gades also around this period*). La Coruña's *'Tower of Hercules'*, which was constructed around the 1st century on the North West point of Iberia (Spain), was on a more adventurous route, and was probably erected to facilitate the safety of vessels, trading between Ireland and Spain. As it is still in sevice, Coruña Light is likely to be the oldest working lighthouse in the World.

Influence of the Romans and their Achievements

Raising wood to a tower's summit as at La Coruña, often by dragging it up inclined ramps, must have been a laborious and strenuous task for the attendants. Similar *'fire-towers'* that were intended to provide a steady light, were often just seen as a pall of smoke, because of the spray dampening the seaward part of the fuel source, with the actual flames lighting up the land.

Roman medals, showing early lighttowers at Boulogne (above) and Apamea. Spitzer Archive

The numerous *'fire-towers'* , established by the Romans, included Ostia (50 AD), Ravenna, Putaeoli, Centumcellae (120 AD) and Leptis Magna on the north coast of Africa, around the same period. Having conquered Gaul (France), a commemoration rubblestone *'light-tower'* was built at Boulogne (44 AD). After adding Britain to its list of conquests, a similar tower was constructed at Dover (England) around 50 AD.

7

The roman pharos at Dover.
Spitzer Archive

Today this structure is a tourist attraction, but the tower at Boulogne collapsed in 1644.

However, it is interesting to note, that from the times of the Romans, when they established the light at Dover, it was not until the end of the 16th century that England had its second official light for the general use of shipping, in the form of a coal fire on top of Tynemouth Castle.

Centuries of Darkness & Chaos

Following the demise of the Roman Empire, its towers fell into decay, with very little advance with maritime lights until the 9th century. One of the prime reasons for this situation, was the belief by most nations, that lights would do more harm as guides for their enemies in times of war. Even then the majority of lights established were mainly of ecclesiastical origin. Apart from these very primitive aids, this left the sailor with astronomy and its extremely unpredictable consequences.

Lack of precise control for keeping a sailing vessel on a desired course, particularly during high winds and tides, was a hard enough problem. But even as the ship was approaching its destination, there was still the difficulty of making a safe landfall. Added to these problems was also the thought that was prevalent in the minds of isolated coastal communities throughout the medieval period, that plundering the cargoes from wrecked or stranded ships, was a legitimate gain under *'custom and descent'*.

Even with the very primitive lights provided by *'religious orders'*, there were still those people who lit false fires, in order to guide seafarers on to dangerous rocks. The lighting of such *'fires'* has been referred to in historical records, to have occurred as early as 700 BC. This clearly indicates that *'light-towers'* of some description were in use around this period. It is also fair to state, that even during these very early years, there were those people whose intention was to thwart the safe progress of the mariner.

The misplacing of lights persisted uncontrolled around England until the 12th century, when Richard Coeur-de-Lion (Richard I) introduced severe punishment for pirates and other heartless people, who were intent on causing ships to be wrecked. Yet this situation still prevailed and became a particular problem for shipping approaching the South-west of England, between the 17th and 18th centuries.

Light Out of Darkness

So dire was the carnage and barbaric pillaging from stranded or wrecked vessels, that the pitiful plight of the helpless sailor exercised the minds among men of conscience, who kept 'genuine' lights burning to keep ships clear from known dangers.

Around the 5th century, St. Dubhan went over from Wales to Ireland, where he established his religious cell on a South-east promontory of the island. He also erected a beacon in the form of a large wooden post, surmounted by an iron fire basket. By means of a ladder, this monk carried up wood or coal to be burnt in the brazier, which was kept ablaze every night until day-break.

Numerous other smaller lights were established by the various cultures around the World, but most to guide ships along recognised routes. These were often erected by the early commercially minded merchants or other opportunists, who exacted payment from the mariners for the usage, yet generally these people were mindless of the actual effectiveness of the lights for navigation.

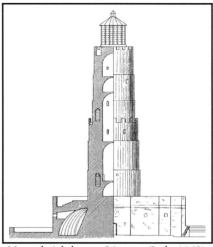

Magnale ighthouse, Livorno (Italy 1163).
Spitzer Archive

A Measure of Control Returns

Law and order began its slow return and prevailed once more, during the start of the 12th century. Trade afloat commenced in two areas, firstly in the Mediterranean, where lighthouses were established at Genoa and Meloria (probably one of the first wave-swept shoals to be surmounted by a light), then in Messina, the crusader port of North-east Sicily, and other harbours around this region that required conspicuous marking. About a century later, the coasts of the Baltic and the North Sea had lights established to assist the expanding sea-trade. Much of this trading was being managed principally by the Hanseatic League, formally organised in 1385, which became a powerful monopoly that safeguarded the interests of merchants up to the 17th century. But its aggressive protection policy saw the League bitterly opposed by many nations, which effectively saw the demise of its dominance. Portugal then became the principal sea-trading power, until it was eventually displaced by Holland and Spain. These two countries virtually controlled the sea-trade, between the Baltic and the West, around the middle of the 16th century. England's participation, although late, was decisive, which necessitated a mayor change in navigating safety.

Order Out of Chaos – Philanthropists or Opportunists

In England, around the 13th century, the Royal prerogative of the *'Divine Right of Kings'* was used to issue *'Seals of Approval'* for official lights around the coastal regions. But the few that were originally awarded were not for humanitarian reasons, only as *'political favours'*.

One of the first *'Seals of Approval'* or *'Royal Letters Patent'*, was given to Baron Simon de Montfort by Henry III in 1265. This Baron was then allowed to erect a light at Winchelsea, to guide shipping into Rye harbour on the Sussex coast (England). He was also authorised to levy shipping for its upkeep. Yet it is known that the *'three'* Royal *'Seals'* were only issued by the King, to stave off a Baronial revolt.

During the 16th century Henry VIII (England) granted a Royal Charter to the Guild of Master Mariners of Deptford Strond, near London. This charitable *'Trinity House'*, of which there were many smaller *'Houses'* around England, became a very powerful Corporation. Over a period of 300 years, Trinity House created a service of beacons, buoys, lighthouses and lightvessels as aids for navigation, that is envied world-wide.

Even with this *'monopolising'* power, the Corporation had to battle with successive monarchs, because of the issuing of Royal Letters Patents to private individuals, which enabled those to erect numerous lights and to levy shipping for their upkeep. By the middle of the 19th century the shipowners were near revolt, because of the very unfair system of imposing the light dues. In 1836 the Parliament of William IV empowered the Corporation to purchase all of the privately owned lights. But the buying of one of these lights, on the Skerries Rock, off Anglesey (North Wales) was bitterly fought over. In 1840 it finally cost Trinity House the *'Princely'* sum of £444,984 (a fortune for this period of time).

Possibly the Finest Lighthouse in the World

Meanwhile the French Port of Bordeaux was trading seriously with Spain, but numerous ships were being wrecked upon a dangerous outcrop of rocks at the mouth of the Gironde estuary. Around the late 12th century a primitive lighted beacon was established on these rocks, and a *'tax'* levied on vessels using this aid. This system of *'light-dues'* was probably the foundation upon which Britain set its levy on ships, to finance its service of aids to navigation.

Around 1356 Edward, the Black

Cordouan lighthouse and fire-tower.
Spitzer Archive

»Sumptuous Cordouan«
K. C. Sutton-Jones Collection

Prince of England, captured John II of France, following a massive battle at Poitiers, and effectively gained the power of Gascony. As a form of celebration for this victory, he had an octagonal tower constructed on the Gironde estuary rocks, with a fire 'chauffeur' erected on its summit. As an act of reverence to the Papal Order, he entrusted the care and maintenance of this light to a hermit.

In 1585 French architect Louis de Foix obtained a concession to erect the new and most magnificent Cordouan tower. It took 26 years to build and was completed during the reign of Henry IV of France. This elaborately designed structure was 60m (197ft) high and consisted of several galleries, that were enriched with sculptured pilasters and friezes. A circular building, about 41m (134ft), in diameter, was constructed around the base of the tower, which contained the keepers apartments, with part of this structure reinforced to break up the force of the sea against the main building

The actual tower contained a chapel and numerous grand apartments, with access to each of its several levels by a grand ornamental helical staircase. It first came into service around October 1611 and is believed to have been lit for the official ceremony by Henry IV.

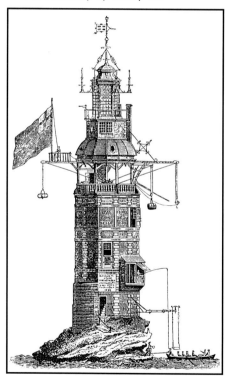

2nd Eddystone tower by Henry Winstanley.
Spitzer Archive

During the reign of Louis XV of France, around 1727, Frenchman M. Bitri is recorded to have been the first person to install a tin covered cupola in the Cordouan tower, as a means of magnifying its coal fired light. In 1789 the tower was drastically altered, which effectively destroyed much of its former architectural beauty. But the outcome of this work rendered it more serviceable as a light-station, which today is regarded as probably the finest in Europe – possibly the World.

The Rock-Tower
'Station Builders'

While the Cordouan is on an exposed site, but close to a river estuary, the establishment of a light upon Eddystone Rock, 9 miles west of Plymouth (England), was a far more daunting task to undertake.

Its bleak location in the English Channel has clearly proved the magnitude of this venture, which has resulted in the construction of a series of five lighthouses. The first tower, built by Henry Winstanley in 1698, devel-

5th (present) Eddystone. K. C. Sutton-Jones Collection

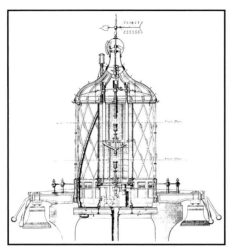

Eddystone lighthouse - helical lantern with 1st order bi-form apparatus and fog bells. Reproduced with kind permission of Trinity

oped numerous practical problems, and during the following year another tower had to be built. But whilst repairs were being carried out by Henry Winstanley and his workforce in 1703, the lighthouse and everyone inside was washed away during a tremendous storm.

The third tower was designed and built by a silk merchant, John Rudyerd, and also constructed of wood, but with close fitting vertical beams, caulked together like the hull of a ship. This lighthouse withstood the ferocity of the English Channel for 40 years, before being destroyed by fire.

A fourth tower was later designed and built by John Smeaton, who is today regarded as the 'Father of the Civil Engineers'. His interlocking granite structure was the great forerunner that set the pattern of tower-rock construction on exposed reefs, well into the 19th century. However, after 123 years the rock beneath Smeaton's tower had been seriously undermined by the ferocity of the sea. In 1882 a superb granite replacement was completed by its designer, James Nicholas Douglass.

This particular engineer was originally part of the Douglass family, that was attached to the civil engineering practise of Walker & Burges. Initially the Father, Nicholas Douglass, entered the Trinity House service as a construction engineer in 1839, before being commissioned by James Walker to supervise the erection of his pile-designed lighthouse on the Bishop Rock (Isles of Scilly). But just before completion of this project, the tower was washed away during a storm in 1847. Later James Walker contracted Nicholas Douglass to supervise the construction of his second Bishop Rock tower, this time built out of solid granite. His son, James Nicholas Douglass, assisted him as the resident engineer.

Following the successful Bishop Rock project, James Nicholas Douglass was commissioned to erect another tower designed by James Walker, situated on the treacherous Smalls Rock. On its completion he then began the construction of the Wolf Rock tower in 1861, but James Walker never saw his designed tower lit, because he suddenly died in 1862. James Nicholas Douglass was then appointed as the first Engineer-in-Chief for Trinity House around the middle of 1863.

Over the next 29 years the achievements of James Nicholas Douglass saw the erection of some twenty towers, which included the designing of the Basses lighthouses on Rocks East of Ceylon (Sri Lanka), Hanois (Channel Islands), a new Eddystone tower in 1882 and the encasing and heightening for the third Bishop Rock lighthouse.

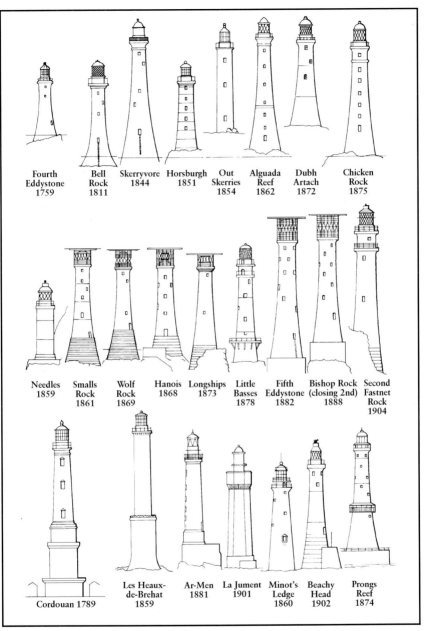

Fourth Eddystone 1759

Bell Rock 1811

Skerryvore 1844

Horsburgh 1851

Out Skerries 1854

Alguada Reef 1862

Dubh Artach 1872

Chicken Rock 1875

Needles 1859

Smalls Rock 1861

Wolf Rock 1869

Hanois 1868

Longships 1873

Little Basses 1878

Fifth Eddystone 1882

Bishop Rock (closing 2nd) 1888

Second Fastnet Rock 1904

Cordouan 1789

Les Heaux-de-Brehat 1859

Ar-Men 1881

La Jument 1901

Minot's Ledge 1860

Beachy Head 1902

Prongs Reef 1874

Rock Towers. K. C. Sutton-Jones Collection

15

After the completion of the Eddystone tower, James Nicholas Douglass was knighted by Queen Victoria, for his *'humanitarian services for the safety of the mariner'*.

The brother of James Nicholas Douglass, William, was responsible for the designing of the Longships tower, off Land's End (England). He later became the Engineer for the Commissioners of Irish Lights, for whom he designed and built the second Fastnet Rock tower, off the South-west of Ireland.

The final member of this distinguished and talented family, was William Tregarthen-Douglass. He worked alongside his father, James Nicholas Douglass, on the construction of the 1882 Eddystone lighthouse. Later he was the resident engineer, who supervised the reconstruction of his father's Bishop Rock lighthouse tower and the Round Island station (Isles of Scilly).

The last rock-based tower of interlocking granite blocks in England, was designed and built by Sir Thomas Matthews in 1902, in front of Beachy Head, off the Sussex coast.

Ireland's Tower-Rock Builders

Apart from the Douglass influence, very little is known about the Halpin family, which consisted of a father and son, who established over 50 lighthouses around Ireland. But prior to his death in 1854, George Halpin (senior) was responsible for the design and construction of the Tuskar Rock tower in 1815. He was also accredited with the towers on The Maidens, Eagle Island and Black Rock Sligo.

His son George Halpin (junior) designed and built the first Fastnet tower around 1854, and other stations, such as the Old Head of Kinsale, Eeragh and Inisheer, that were erected on the Aran Islands.

Expansion in tower-rock construction around Ireland began in earnest, following the formation of the Commissioners of Irish Lights. However, for many years after this Corporation was established, it was still better known as the Dublin Ballast Board.

Continued French Influence

Many notable towers have been constructed around France, apart from the *'grandiose'* Cordouan. Of the many builders, Frenchman Leonce Reynard introduced a similar interlocking stone design as employed by John Smeaton. But the principle of construction for withstanding the sea's might was different. Yet this system was successful, as proven at Heaux-de-Brehat, Ar Men, La Joument and Les Four, where work on these structures called for exceptional endurance by both, the builders and the workforce, who erected them against the prevailing elements.

Rapid Progress in Scotland

Safeguarding the mariner from the coastal dangers around Scotland was addressed with the establishment of the Commissioners of the Northern Lights in 1786. Originally the designer and builder of the Hunstanton lighthouse (England), Ezekiel Walker, was invited by the Board of Commissioners, to design and erect the four new planned lightstations. Instead this honour was awarded to one of his pupils, Thomas Smith, who Walker had tutored in civil engineering and methods of construction.

Thomas Smith was also a *'municipal lamp-maker'*, and with his reputation for various engineering projects around Glasgow, he was appointed as the Commissioners first *'Engineer'*. His stepson, Robert Stevenson, became his assistant. Yet there is very little mention of architect Robert Kay, who prepared all of the working drawings for the new Scottish lighthouses, based upon the designs of Thomas Smith.

Robert Stevenson also became the founder of the famous Scottish dynasty of lighthouse engineers, and by 1811 he had designed and established the tidal-influenced Bell Rock tower. Over a period of 150 years, the Stevenson family designed and erected more than 85 lighthouses around Scotland, its outer Isles, and on the Isle of Man. Among these were the renowned, isolated rock-based towers of Dubh Artach (1872) and Chicken Rock (1875); and it was at Skerryvore (1844), that Alan Stevenson relied upon the weight of the lower part of the granite block-work, to resist lateral displacement by the force of the waves without resorting to the expensive dovetailing of the individual blocks of granite. The force of such seas during winter gales could be as high as 20,000kg per square metre!

The Stevenson *'family'* also contributed, to a major degree, in the design and application of lighting apparatus, along with Alan Brebner, not only around Scotland, but in lightstations in South-east Asia, India and Japan.

This record of achievement by the Stevensons, for their contribution to maritime safety, has yet to be surpassed.

A Variety of Sites & Conditions

At the time of opening the Suez Canal in 1870, several lightstations had been established on coral reefs and along the desert coastline of the Red Sea. Many of these construction projects were undertaken by William Parkes and equipped by French lighthouse manufacturers. Along with Charles William Scott, an engineer from Sunderland (England), he designed and built the masonry tower at Zafarana Point and the two lattice structures of wrought-iron and teak, on the Ashrafi and Daedalus reef (Abu Kizan).

Lighthouse construction on-shore varied considerably and was dependant upon the elevation required above sea level, or the bearing strength of the ground available. This was especially the case in soft sea-bed or swamp areas, where the system of employing *'screw piles'* proved successful. This method was originally invented by the blind engineer Alexander Mitchell, from Belfast (Ireland), in 1837.

In most uninhabited or isolated areas, the factory-manufactured tower was chosen,

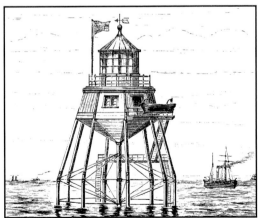

Mitchell's screw-pile structure (Maplin Sands).
Spitzer Archive

French iron tower in the vicinity of the Red Sea, built around 1870. K. C. Sutton-Jones Collection

with many supplied in sections to be bolted together on-site. One of the first pile lighthouses, which utilized the Mitchell screw invention, was the Maplin station on the North-side of the mouth of the River Thames (England), in 1838.

Other adaptions of the screw-piled cast-iron lighthouses were successfully erected by Alexander Gordon (1802–68), with the first of his projects being on Morant Point, at the east end of Jamaica. Another even larger tower was established within the focus of the Atlantic hurricanes, in the centre of the Island of Bermuda. This structure stands a majestic 32m (106ft) high and consists of seven storeys. It was first brought into service on the 9th October 1845.

Around 1868 the French Government had an iron pile lighthouse erected in the entrance to Port Noumea, New Caledonia (South Pacific). It stood over 45m (147ft) high and was first displayed at the Paris Exhibition of 1867. A similar tower was also erected on the Roches Douvres, in the English Channel.

Numerous similar screw-piled towers were successfully established throughout the former Colonial dependancies, Norway and South Africa. Today's equivalent of these lattice towers are made of reinforced plastic modules and are employed extensively around the World.

Great Ingenuity of Construction

Modern civil engineering principles have been employed to great effect in recent years. Dungeness, on the South Coast of England, is one such example. This station is located along a stretch of shore-line, which 'grows' towards the sea under the tidal influences. An observer off the Point would detect three lighthouses, each introduced over many years to keep pace with the extending shore-line. In total there have been five towers established at Dungeness since 1615, the first of which only lasted for 20 years. But even with the evermoving shore, the water off the Point is still deep enough to allow large ships to pass quite close to the Kent coast.

In 1904 another lighthouse was established, but the arrival of two nuclear power stations made this station inoperative. Not because of the shifting land, but by reason of these generation-plants, that partially obscured its light. The most recent lighthouse was erected in 1961 and designed by Ronald Ward & Partners, with its construction supervised by Philip Hunt, the Engineer-in-Chief of Trinity House. It was erected to a height of 40m (130ft), and constructed out of pre-stressed concrete rings, manufactured by Spun Concrete Ltd. of Rye Harbour (England).

Up to the 1960's various *'innovative'* ideas had been put forward, to provide suitable structures off-shore, that would replace the stationary lightvessels. Even up to this period the equipment required to ensure the complete security of operation aboard a lightship, in an unattended mode, had yet to be proven. With these vessels requiring two crews (*one on duty – the other on relief*), the cost of manning, relieving the station and maintenance, was considered to be prohibitive.

Another method of establishing a tower on a soft sandbank was attempted first by the German Authorities at the Roter Sand, a point some 50 kilometres from Bremerhaven, between the mouth of the Weser River and the island of Heligoland. Funded by a tax on shipping, the design features a large steel caisson upon which the lighthouse and its apparatus would be installed. The first attempt to take a large steel caisson out into the North Sea's gales failed, but a modification to an oval section, for the replacement, enabled the unit to be towed upright and sunk onto and into the sand by means of ballast, assisted by men excavating the sand from within. The design and site works were accomplished in 1882–1885, sixty years before the lightvessel replacement programme, undertaken by Robert Gellerstad, a brilliant engineer in the Swedish Service, who devised a submersible tower, formed out of concrete. It wa constructed ashore on wooden supports, launched like a ship, towed out to its specified location and then sunk on to a prepared shoal. His design also ensured that its outer shell was

Pre-stressed tower, Dungeness, Kent, England, under construction and completed.

Photographs with kind permission of Edward Carpenter

19

Kish Bank lighthouse, Co. Dublin, Ireland.
With kind permission of Commissioners of Irish Lights

deep enough, for the structure to be stabilized by ballast.

Once the outer shell of this type of pre-formed tower was set into position, a cylindrical shaft, nestling inside, was raised by hydraulic power. The other advantage of this *'innovative'* design, was that the lantern, lighting apparatus and associated helipad, could be safely installed while the structure was being completed. Once the inner shaft was raised to its designated height above sea level, the hollow lower section would be filled with vibrated shingle and a special concrete composition that hardened under water. The lower, outer perimeter of the main shell was formed as a ring of *'teeth'*, similar to a wood saw. The purpose of this design was, to ensure that the structure cut into the seabed, to provide a permanent anchor for the lightstation.

This type of structure was established around the Baltic Sea to replace many of the manned lightvessels. A larger version was adopted at Kish Bank, off the East coast of Ireland. In 1971 the Royal Sovereign lightvessel was taken off station and replaced by a pre-constructed concrete submersible unit, designed by Sir William Halcrow & Partners. It was constructed in a special dry-dock at Newhaven by Christiani & Nielsen, under the supervision of Ian Clinghan for Trinity House. The siting of this new tower was off the Sussex coast near Eastbourne (England).

Although the demise of the lightvessel seemed imminent, they had to be stationed to guard certain off-shore areas around England an Wales. Notably the Goodwin Sands off Kent, Royal Sovereign Bank and many other shoals or isolated rocks, where the establishment of lighthouse structures had not been economically practical at the time.

The All Important Light

There has been much advancement in the various methods of providing a suitable and sustainable illumination for a *'guiding'* light. Up to the 19th century the light normally comprised an open grate that burnt coal or wood. Tallow candles set into a candelabra, with as many as 60 being lit at any one time, was often the early type of lighting system in many of the larger stations. Even up to 1759 the lack of lighting technology was emphasised, when John Smeaton first lit his Eddystone tower.

An attempt to improve the open-fired braziers, by shielding them with a glazed lantern, failed because of insufficient ventilation. The South Foreland lighthouse, on the coast of Kent (England), was enclosed by a lantern around 1683, but lack of proper attendance saw the structure razed to the ground. This same station had another tower erected around 1732, with its coal-fired light surrounded by sash-

Roter Sand lighthouse, off the River Weser estuary, Germany. Photograph with kind permission of Volker Siemers

Early parabolic reflector by Thomas Smith. Photograph Karl R. Spitzer

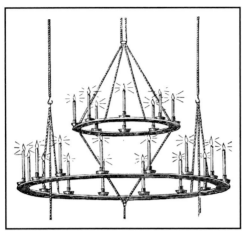

Smeaton's Eddystone chandelier.
Spitzer Archive

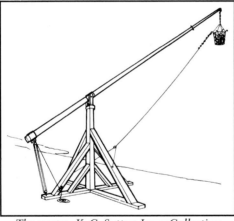

The swape. K. C. Sutton-Jones Collection

type windows. Large leather bellows were pumped all through the night, to ensure there was adequate air circulation. But this idea soon proved unsuitable, with the light reverting to an open fire around 1790.

Meanwhile the *'Swape'* was being installed in great numbers along the Baltic coasts. These contraptions consisted of a fire-basket suspended from an inclined, pivoted pole, for ease of refuelling, and supported upon a tripod frame. This apparatus also permitted the *'light'* to be swung horizontally and vertically, in order to enhance its illuminated signal. Although extremely cheap to produce, the *'Swape'* was taken out of service, because it proved dangerous to operate and showered its attendants with red-hot embers.

Improved Performance – Positive Recognition

Duplication and even triplication of *'fire-towers'*, as a means to render the stations distinguishable from each other, was an expensive necessity. Yet up to the 1800's, *'lightstations'* had not become so numerous as to make this situation essential in more than a few instances.

In reality, up to 1600, there were only about 50 lights that aided navigation in Northern Europe. But identifying one light or *'fire-tower'* from another was a problem, until extra structures were erected to provide two (*as at the Lizard Point - England*) or a group of three lights (*as established at the Casquets – Channel Islands*), as a positive means of recognition by the mariner.

Shipping increased dramatically during the 18th century and greatly stimulated the need for inventiveness to improve the station's performance and to render its light more distinct. When a fire burned brightly, it provided a considered visible range for the mariner to fix a position, but this was expensive in fuel consumption and hard labour.

Reflectors

Spherical and parabolic reflectors came in around 1763, as independent units behind a light source. It was at this time that William Hutchinson, a Liverpool Dock-Master, devised the first parabolic reflectors for an English lighthouse. His method consisted of some small catoptric reflectors, made of polished tin, with larger ones formed out of concaved wood, surfaced with facets of mirrors. This method was then followed by a spate of competing reflectors, made of mirrors set on to metal, which were devised by Frenchman M. Teulére and fellow countryman M. Lenoir. However, Lenoir is accredited as producing the first parabolic reflector using silvered copper around 1780.

The great advance in lighthouse illumination came in 1784, when Aimé Argand, a Swiss discoverer, patented a smokeless oil lamp with a hollow-wick and glass-chimney. His exceptional contribution to light-sources became the standard method, used in various forms, for over 100 years.

In 1786, Thomas Smith devised his own version of the Hutchinson's reflectors for use in Scottish lighthouses. However, his method came up against several criticisms, because the viewers felt that the larger pieces of mirror, used in these units, effectively distorted the light. Yet these mirrors were intended to share the horizontal arc of the light by overlapping the beams. One of the first arrangements of these reflectors was installed at the Pentland Skerries (Scotland). Each of these units was illuminated by a single flat-wick oil lamp, that burnt either colza (rape-

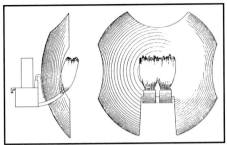

Spherical reflector at La Héve lighthouse, France 1781. Spitzer Archive

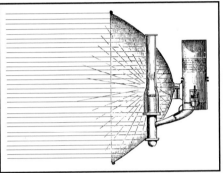

Parabolic reflector and Argand burner. Spitzer Archive

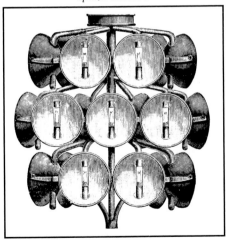

Revolving multi-mirror oil lighted reflectors. Spitzer Archive

23

Revolving reflector light, Cape Bonavista lighthouse, NF, Canada. First used at Isle of May lighthouse, Scotland. Photograph Karl R. Spitzer

seed) or sperm oils. [*see picture on page 21*]

Other stations around Scotland were also fitted with these new reflectors, by men who often worked in extremely harsh conditions. On one occasion Robert Stevenson worked alongside these men, but before the project was completed, he received instruction from the Commissioners to return to Edinburgh. A short while later, however, the vessel was wrecked while returning to the lightstation, with all of his colleagues drowned.

Recognition

The means to impart a recognisable flashing characteristic for a particular lightstation was solved in 1781, with an apparatus installed at Carlsten on Sweden's east coast. Reflectors, with a light-source produced by wide-wick type oil lamps, were assembled on to a central shaft, then rotated as a complete unit by a weight-driven mechanism. Although this drive system could be considered as a clock, it was in fact a mechanism that comprised of a simple heavy weight, hung below the light apparatus. Calculation was carefully made to ensure that the drive weight was slightly heavier than the rotating assembly, with coins used to provide the fine adjustment. A basic ratchet-style lever also assisted with the control of the falling weight.

This type of lighting apparatus was capable of providing a slowly flashing character. Each beam of light, from its panel of lamps and reflectors, had a combined intensity of about 12,000 candelas, with a visible distance of nearly 15

24

nautical miles in average weather conditions. When compared with today's standards, this flashing sequence was extremely long.

What were the Basic Needs for the Sailor?
With effective control of the helm limited during the days of sail, landfall knowledge, and a positive means to fix a vessel's position by compass, were extremely important. Visibility was also a priority, which had to be possible for a 'crow's nest' observer from more than 20 nautical miles away.

For illumination to travel this distance, it needed to have an effective intensity exceeding 100,000 candelas. But due to the relatively slow progress of the sailing vessels, this light only required a repetitive characteristic of no more than once every one or two minutes.

A vessel sailing across the Atlantic Ocean from America during the wintertime, would probably be driven by strong westerly winds and under a 'leaden' sky. Any observations of the sun or stars could be denied, perhaps over the larger portion of the voyage.

Under such conditions, when a landfall was finally reached, it could be anywhere from between the Northern parts of the Outer Hebrides to the coast of Spain. Accordingly lighthouses were liberally established along the Western Shores of Ireland, Wales, the South West of England, France, Spain and Portugal, as a means to mark the off-shore dangers and to highlight distinctive promontories.

Following the advent of steam-powered ships around 1820, the controls of a vessel's helm became more positive. But these changes also brought about faster and straighter courses, being followed by shipping, which dictated the need for a more frequent repetition of a light's character to 30, 20, 15 or 10 second intervals. Its visible range had to be at least 22 nautical miles, because this was the distance a steam-powered vessel could traverse within one or two hours. To obtain this desired luminous range, a light required an intensity of between 300,000 and 800,000 candelas.

Development of Clear Weather Aids to Navigation
Larger rotating assemblies with panels of catoptric reflectors, illuminated by oil-burning Argand lamps, continued to be employed in lighthouses around the World well into the 19th century. Some of these assemblies contained up to eight reflectors and associated lamps on each panel face. In turn these panels were capable of producing an intensity of about 50,000 candelas at the summit of many lighthouses.

Around 1819 the inventive application of the Science of Optics, particularly by Frenchman Augustin Fresnel, brought about the introduction of the dioptric annular lens. This optical expert split up a 'Bull's Eye' glass lens into annular rings or prisms, which, when mounted together at a specific setting, refracted the errant rays of the illuminant into a horizontal beam. In turn this produced a beam, that was the same width as the light-source and the height of the lens in total. The rings or prisms had a common vertical axis through the light source. But this could be arranged horizontally with the prisms generated radially around the axis, into a panel of rings. When rotated around the light-source at its focal centre, it produced a concentrated horizontal beam of illumination, that swept past an observer's eye as an extremely intense flash of light.

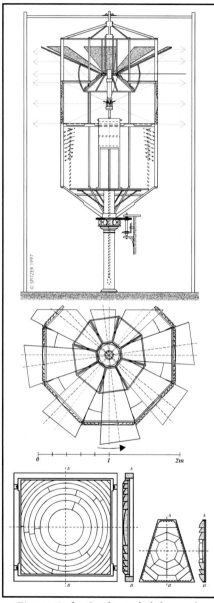

First optic for Cordouan lighthouse, by
Augustin Fresnel, 1823.
Drawing by H.-G. Spitzer

If a number of similar optical panels were made to share the total angle, sub-tended by the light-source, it became possible to produce characters of a single, or groups of 2, 3 or 4 flashes within a timed sequence. Early optics combined a *'fixed'* with a *'flashing'* succession, by superimposing the *'flash panels'* generated around the horizontal axis, above a series of prisms surrounding the vertical axial. However, rays from a light-source, radiating above a certain angle from the axis, would be reflected off the collecting surface of the prismatic rings. But these rays could be diverted on to a horizontal plane by the addition of mirrors, to enhance the beams from the main rotating panels of annular rings. Thomas Stevenson devised this method of optical mirrors and prisms, which was installed in the Skerryvore lighthouse on its completion in 1844.

French glass manufacturers were the first to enter the field of supplying prismatic optics, with ingenious rotating assemblies constructed in many forms, to suit the site requirements at numerous lightstations, including several in the *'British Isles'*. The names of Barbier & Bénard, Henry Lepaute and Sautter Harle, to state a few, became world-famous in their time.

Cookson of Newcastle-upon-Tyne started up the industry in England, but the company that rose rapidly as a competitor after 1850, was Chance Brothers of Birmingham. In the glass founding business, many famous names from both sides of the English Channel were involved. Apart from Chance Brothers (England) there was Saint Gobain of France, and Wilhelm Weule of Germany, who excelled in the production of specialist glass.

There were also many individuals

26

who played a major role in the technological field of optical application and gained world-wide acclaim for their contributions. These included Allard, Blaise, Blondel, Bourdelles, LeTourneau, Ribiere and Tabouret (France), Körte and Pintsch (Germany) and James Chance, Hopkinson and Kenward (England) and Thomas Stevenson and Brebner, to name just a few.

Value of Intensities & Majestic Optics

At this stage in the development of major lights at sea, the source of illumination was the wick oil burner, using either sperm or colza as its fuel. Around this time the luminance was about 2 candelas per cm². Between 1870 and 1912, this intensity was considerably increased to 50 candelas per cm², following the introduction of kerosene (*paraffin*). But the lens panels for condensing these low values of intensity, during the early years, had to be of enormous proportions, which saw many majestic, or even extravagant assemblies being manufacture.

By this period, the area of glass in a single lens panel needed to deliver 300,000 candelas per flash from a wick source. The apparatus supplied in 1882, for the Eddystone light, required a focus of 920mm, with 12 panels set in 6 pairs of a double flash sequence. This assembly rotated slowly on a roller carriage, at one revolution in 180 seconds, to provide a group of flashes every 30 seconds.

The falling weight that powered the Eddystone clockwork turntable mechanism, had to be rewound twice an hour. This proved to be an extremely arduous task, with the physical labour being required by the keepers.

At the Bishop Rock (Isles of Scilly), an even larger apparatus, which consisted of a '*bi-form*' assembly, was needed. This unit comprised one lens apparatus above the other, which each tier having 5 sets of 2

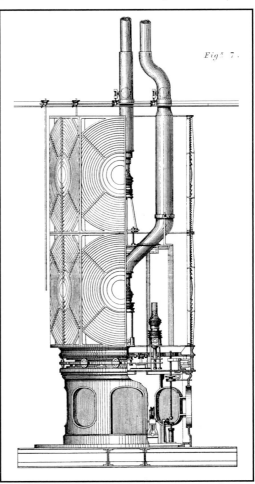

Fig. 7.

Round Island hyperradial bi-form optic – similar to Bishop Rock. With kind permission of Trinity House

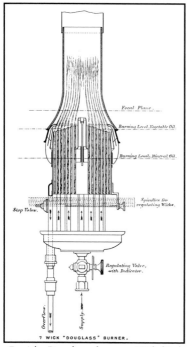

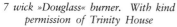

*7 wick »Douglass« burner. With kind
permission of Trinity House*

*»Cleaning the lamp«
Spitzer Archive*

panels, with a 1330mm focus. In turn this complete assembly rotated to produce a double flash every minute. Its light-source had to be very wide, in order to provide an appreciable length of flash that could readily be seen by the distant viewer, with the whole of the apparatus only rotating once in 300 seconds. This particular optic was designed by *'Uncle Bill Richey'* W. F. A. Richey, who was much respected by all concerned at Chance Brothers during this period. An oil burner with 8 concentric wicks was required for each tier of the lenses.

Heat generated by these massive oil burners can only be imagined. But it has been alleged that, before extinguishing in the morning, the keepers would cook the breakfast of eggs and bacon in a frying pan placed over the flames.

One part of this magnificent bi-form assembly is now preserved in the Trinity House National Lighthouse Centre at Penzance, Cornwall (England).

Protection from the Elements

A majestic optical apparatus, with its vast areas of prismatic glass weighing many tonnes, called for a protective lantern enclosure of truly robust design. This was especially important when Atlantic gales of force 11 or 12 drove the sea against the rock, sending mountainous volumes of spray as high as 40m (131ft) up the side of a lighthouse. The two multi-wick burners inside the lenses were greedy for oxygen and produced much heat. It was therefore imperative that the lantern provided

28

Portland Bill, UK, optic with 4 panels and catadioptric mirror.   Photograph Karl R. Spitzer

Roller bearings of first order optic for Point Reyes lighthouse, California (USA), manufactured by Barbier & Fenestre, Paris 1867.   Photograph Karl R. Spitzer

Douglass 14ft lantern for Bishop Rock lighthouse at Chance Brothers lighthouse works.
K. C. Sutton-Jones Collection

adequate ventilation, to ensure clarity for the revolving beams of light passing through 12mm thick glass.

These panes of glass are curved 'Diamond' and 'Half Diamond' in shape and held in place by a heavy 'cage' constructed of gun-metal bars, all very skillfully fitted and assembled with great care. This enormous 'glazed cage' is bolted down on to the upper flange, or sill, of the 'Murette' (or *circular wall section*). This comprises of segmental cast-iron units, approximately 2.4m (8ft) high, which are bolted together at their end frames to form the heavy cylindrical assembly. In turn this assembled hollow unit is bolted to the lantern room floor joists. Part of this pedestal base is formed into a curved door that provides access on to the gallery. Its interior face is lined with metal sheets, fitted with adjustable vents.

Above the glazed 'cage' is a cast-iron gutter and supports for the large domed roof, which consists of gun-metal or iron rafters, covered with thick sheets of copper. An inner copper-lining is fixed to the upper portion of the assembly, which provides an air passage into a very large dome-topped 'drum' ventilator, surmounting the roof. Large bore vent-pipes carry the combustion gases and heat away from each of the two wick-burners into the roof ventilator.

To complete the ventilation process, there are vents fitted on the external face of the murette, which admit air to be drawn by the heat, rising from the oil burners through the void inside the cast-iron base. Aperatures in the upper flanges or sills, direct the flow of air over the inner surface of the lantern glazing, then upwards into the channels between the rafters and roof sheeting, to exit through the drum ventilator. This innovative design kept the glazing generally free of condensation and misting, and proved to be a brilliant application of ventilation engineering.

Three Cardinal Advances

As the very large lens-panels revolved *'magnificently'* but slowly upon a carriage mounted on roller bearings, the motive power was provided by a clockwork mechanism, driven by falling weights. Yet this system required frequent and very laborious rewinding periods by the keepers. Next came three important innovations, which took the oil-burning apparatus and its associated optical drive units to the pinnacle of achievement.

The ponderous roller bearing pedestal was replaced by a turntable, floating in an annular trough containing mercury. This resulted in a faster speed of rotation and introduced an optical apparatus with fewer, yet larger panels of glass prisms. In turn this produced the station's assigned light characteristic with more frequent repetition. So effective was the mercury system, that it provided a virtual friction free surface, when compared to the former roller bearings. Its introduction, plus a new gearing assembly for the clocks, also greatly reduced the laborious rewinding of the heavy weight by the keepers.

Another innovation was to place the optical axis of some panels away from their centres, which enable flashes in a 'group flash' character to recur closer together to make the sequence easier to recognise.

Illumination, with oil as its fuel, was brought to the peak of luminosity and suitability with the introduction of the Kitson incandescent burner. Initially the kerosene, or paraffin, was fed under pressure through vaporising tubes into a retort below a mantle. A small methylated spirit burner was used as its temporary heating source, that was lit under the retort. When the oil turned into a fuming white gas, it was lit above the fine meshed mantle to produce a homogeneous light. This uniform illumination was far more compact than the multi-wick burner with a higher

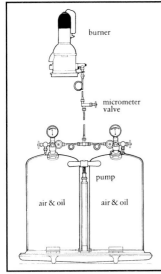

Above:
Chance »PV-burner« installation.
K. C. Sutton-Jones Collection

Keeper working the pressure
pump. Spitzer Archive

31

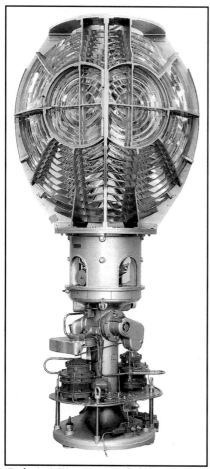

Dalén's AGA automatic lighthouse using acetylene.
K. C. Sutton-Jones Collection

luminance. Some of the heated gas returned down a separate *'Bunsen'* pipe, located close to the vaporising tube, and maintained the production process automatically. The first mantles to be used were pre-formed and stiffened with collodion, but later the autoform mantle came into service, which automatically assumed its required shape once the gas was ignited. This allowed the mantles to be stored in larger quantities with greater ease.

Mantles used on, what became known as, the *'PVB'* (*Petroleum Vapour Burner*), were of 35mm to 110mm diameter and employed according to the character of the particular optical apparatus.

Objectively the mariner needed to observe the character of a light, with the length of flash exceeding 0.2 seconds (*any shorter flash would effect visual reception*) Therefore the light intensity through the optic had to be concentrated properly to obtain the required length of flash. The actual flash length is a combination of the focal size of the lens, its speed of rotation, and the width of the light-source.

The final outcome of all of these innovative refinements to the optics and their associated mechanisms, produced a quick repetitive group-flashing character of lights, where they came in easily recognisable patterns. With large optical assemblies, the effective intensity of the light approached one million candelas.

All of these accomplishments effectively reduced the oil consumption to around 600ml (*just over one pint*) per hour. Also the weight drive, for the clockwork mechanism, only required rewinding once every four hour watch.

Magnificence in Attended Lighthouses

The zenith for the fully manned major lighthouse had now arrived. Those with many years experience in pharological matters, looked upon the *'Era of Magnificence'* to be exactly right for the navigation requirements of that period. All of the lighting apparatus and its associated assemblies were solidly built, mostly from sea atmosphere resistant gun-metal, cast-iron or copper; material that was intended to

32

last *'Forever'*. In fact they were superseded due to economical and navigation requirements, just over a century after being introduced.

Originally the clockwork mechanism needed very little maintenance, nor did it require the skills of a highly specialised technician if a mechanical problem arose. This was always overcome by the ingenuity and adaptability of the keepers. Its operation was virtually silent without engine noise, it smelt abdominably of paraffin and was, although in its own right a *'work of engineering art'*, a monster to clean. But at least it was cleaned, which cannot happen so thoroughly with the modern unmanned stations.

Other Sources of Light

Paraffin vapour burners were employed universally until recently. In Ireland three PVB mantles were clustered into a single source, which gave a wider area of light for increasing the length of flash required and also reduced the extinction of the illumination due to mantle breakage.

Coal gas was introduced in Ireland and other places around the World by J. R. Wigham. In some cases the station had its own gas works and holder, such as Howth Bailey near Dublin. This system produced a wide light-source for allowing a much longer flash. But with multi-lens assemblies, each unit required its own gas burner. Lenses were even arranged in *'Quadriform'* and lit according to the external visibility around the lightstation.

Acetylene Gas

In Canada and Sweden, the era for employing acetylene gas as a light-source commenced almost simultaneously in 1904. By this time the German *'Pintsch'* buoy lanterns had gained a good reputation. Leopold Willson, the inventor of the original acetylene process, utilized this lantern and incorporated a very bright burner, with its gas generator mounted inside of the buoy. Many of those introduced for navigation, entered service in Canada and South America. Unfortunately this type of apparatus produced some very spectacular explosive accidents.

Two Frenchmen, Claude and Hess, discovered a system of storing and transporting compressed acetylene gas by dissolving it in acetone and holding it in steel cylinders. This method was successfully used in Swedish lighthouses in which a continuous acetylene flame was required. But there was still the danger of spectacular explosions.

What was needed, was to refine the storage

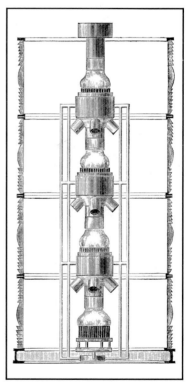

Wigham quadriform gas burner.
Spitzer Archive

Acetylene storage cylinders. Spitzer Archive

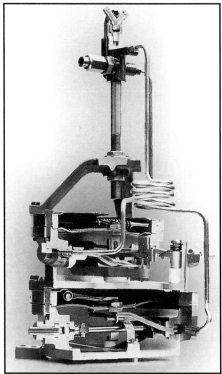

Cut-away photograph of AGA gas flasher.
K. C. Sutton-Jones Collection

system and develop a means of employing the gas economically, and then only during the hours of darkness. Gustaf Dalén made a commendable name for himself by solving these problems with the invention firstly of the acetylene gas flasher, and then of the *'Sun Valve'*. The latter was based upon the expansion of metal when heated. A black matt-finished rod was surrounded by a group of highly polished rods that reflected the infrared rays on to the central bar. With the centre rod held at the top, its lower portion expanded downwards and operated a small valve which controlled the flow of gas.

The unique feature of the Dalén invention was the fact, that it was not reliant upon direct sunlight. All that was required was the infrared spectrum of light that is present during the day time.

These devices effectively extended the unattended service time of the apparatus on a buoy or beacon to over a year, without further attention being required. The invention of the sun valve earned Gustaf Dalén the Nobel Prize in 1912.

The Advent
& Application of Electricity

Regarded as the *'Ultimate Panacea'*, electricity was to become the prime illuminant in lighthouses. Because the carbon arc principle was being used in other fields, such as Admiralty signalling, due to its very high brilliance, it was believed to be the ideal answer to lighthouse illumination.

Although the light-source from a carbon arc lamp was extremely bright, its small beam demanded a special optical apparatus. Firstly the rays of light were collected by the prisms of a lens over the appropriate vertical angle. However, this strip of light had to be spread horizontally into an acceptable flash (*or groups of flashes*), by employing a rotating '*cage*' of vertical collecting prisms. These types of complicated and expensive assemblies were notably installed at the Lizard, South Foreland, Souter Point and St. Catherine's in England. Also it was utilized in the Isle of May lighthouse, at the entrance of the Firth of Forth in Scotland.

Yet the required power system demanded the establishment of too many other services at an isolated station. These included coal-fired, steam-driven generators with ample supplies of pure water and the costly, labour intensified maintenance of all the equipment. This resulted in a reversion of policy by the various Lighthouse Authorities, despite the availability of Faraday's discovery of electricity and the re-introduction of the PVB system which remained in service until the post World War II era.

Similar notions, with regards to the use of electricity, emerged in the 1960's, when the use of Lasers and the Xenon Arc were thought to offer viable advantages. At a later stage of development, after intensive research was undertaken, these types of light-sources were to play a future part in another field of navigation.

There was not only a great deal of interest in finding electric lamps which could replace the PVB units, or to improve the existing luminous range, but the need to utilize a means for employing localised mains power supplies. South Foreland lighthouse near Dover was used as an experimental testing ground for several aspects in the improvement of the signal for the mariner, and for the quest to obtain suitable electric lamps. Numerous filament arrangements were tested, to see if they replicated the homogeneous illumination from an incandescent PVB mantle.

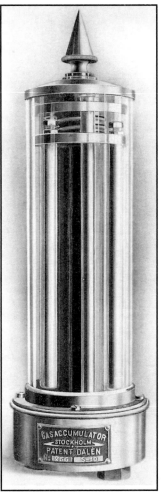

Early Dalén »Sun-valve«.
Spitzer Archive

Many large original optics (*1330mm focus Hyperadial*) constructed for use with the multi-wick burner (*150mm diameter*), had the '*dioptric*' prisms set on the focal centre. But because of the obstruction created by the base of the oil burner, some '*catadioptric* ' (*refracting/reflecting*) prisms, in the lower area of the optic, were focused on points as far as 40mm from the actual focal centre of the lens. Also to trim or attend the burner, the keeper had to enter the optic from below and this called for the use of '*straight down*' lower catadioptric prisms to permit access for his '*girth*'. Accordingly, an electric lamp would require a very large filament structure, in order to replicate the original light-source performance.

Top left: Canadian standard GRP tower, Cape Spencer, NB, Canada. Top right: Small AGA lantern with moulded plastic lens. K. C. Sutton-Jones Collection. Second order optic, St. Catherine's lighthouse, Isle of Wight, England. Colour photographs Karl R. Spitzer

While having a higher luminosity than an oil burner, the filament presented no homogeneous source, but caused patterns to be produced in the projected beam. Many types of filament bulbs were manufactured, each with their own strange names. There was the *'Large Cage'*, *'Bunch'*, *'Double Cones Base to Base'*, also the *'Bi-Planar'* with two vertical frames of filaments at 90° to each other, plus the *'Stanocil'* in which a filament was placed inside a cylinder of diffusing material. All of these arrangements were fitted inside large globes of special glass, and even if produced in modest quantities, it would have made them very expensive to purchase. In reality none of the methods would make the lamp producer a fortune, and were therefore regarded as a nuisance to supply in the comparatively small quantities required.

However, optics up to a 700mm focus, which had been constructed for employing the PVB, were found to be satisfactory when illuminated by lamps of 1.5kW to 3.5kW rating, and provided many years of adequate, though expensive service. It is only recently that the Metal Halide Arc

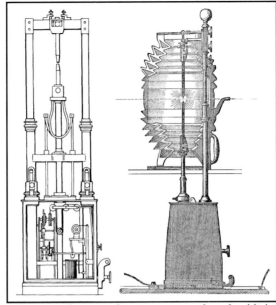

Electric arc lamp · Electric apparatus for a fixed light
K. Sutton-Jones Collection   ·   Spitzer Archive

Magneto electric machine, formerly used at
Souter Point lighthouse. Spitzer Archive

Lamp, rated at between 0.4 and 2kW, has been found suitable as a replacement for the PVB. Its luminance, though somewhat less than the filament, has a mantle-like homogeny with a long life. It is also nearly the ideal light-source for converting such optical assemblies with 375mm to 920mm focus, especially for the units made since

1930, which had prisms of a greater focal accuracy.

Before the advent of Radar, there were sound reasons for maximising the observations of a land-fall, for under high clouds the light could be seen from a great distance by the mariner because of its reflection in the sky.

The luminance of a filament lamp could be as much as 10 times greater than the PVB, but the high *'Stationary Intensity'* of the optic would be attenuated by a shorter length of flash, resulting from a narrower light source. Even so, the *'Effective Intensity'* could be several millions of candelas. In general there was an enormous excess of intensity that was no longer required or could be utilized, as events have since proved.

World-wide Conversion Programme

Although many light stations in the developed countries were electrified in the 1930's, the majority of these conversions took place after World War II. During these hostilities there were several areas under conflict, where lightstations became badly damaged, destroyed or neglected. However, through this war-time period the local inhabitants became knowledgeable and adept at servicing diesel engines and various electrical plant.

There was a clamour at isolated lightstations following this War, for the availability of electricity to illuminate dwellings and for operating radio, then later television receivers. This situation was particularly a prime consideration in the tropical areas of South East Asia. Accordingly, after years under Japanese occupation, the major lightstations in these countries were re-equipped with an optic, that was generally smaller than the originally installed apparatus. In turn these new optical assemblies were then illuminated with filament lamps and rotated by electric motors set in duplicate (*one mains and a standby in reserve*).

The power source was produced by three identical diesel engine driven generators, one in operation, another on standby, even if the third is under routine servicing. Yet with electrical generation plants employed in sequence, the overhaul period was prolonged. Where a local power supply was available, it was employed, but supported by a diesel driven standby generator in case of mains failure.

Semi-watched Stations

Switchgear design had advanced during the Second World War, but compared to the developed countries, it was now expected to endure the humid tropical conditions and therefore needed special protection. For this reason these lightstations became known as *'Semi-Watched'*, although with a bit of innovation they could have been fully automatic. Nevertheless this system was a step in that direction.

The power plants at these stations were started by a push-button or switch, as soon as a photoelectric daylight sensor initiated the ringing of a loud alarm. Sensors for water temperature, sump-oil pressure and various other factors, would shut down the plant, with an alarm informing the keepers that the reserve unit had to be started. If there was a total power system failure, an oil lamp could be temporarily reinstated manually, with a mantle pre-set in focus with the optical assembly. For particularly isolated land-based, rock, or island stations, a refinement was introduced, whereby a clockwork rotation mechanism had an electric motor installed to automatically rewind its heavy drive weight. In the event of total power failure, or lack of diesel fuel for the engines, the weight could still be rewound by the original manual method.

For this time it was no longer necessary for the keepers to keep their nightly vigil in the lantern or service room. Their household used paraffin for cooking, with the electricity employed for the lighting and radio.

This semi-watched method worked well for over 20 years, especially in the majority of cases where the system was initially introduced. These included such lightstations in Aden, Bermuda, Borneo, Burma (*now Myanmar*), Ceylon (*Sri Lanka*), Dutch East Indies, Egypt, Ghana, Liberia, Mauritius, Nigeria, Peninsular Malaysia (*now Sabah, Sarawak and Indonesia*), Philippines, Sierra Leone, Singapore, Sudan and Trinidad. Similar optical assemblies were also provided throughout Australia, India and New Zealand.

Buoys & Beacons

Meanwhile the buoys and beacons remained operated and re-equipped with the ever faithful, reliable and dependable acetylene gas systems, manufactured principally by AGA and PINTSCH. The contract for lights and other navigational aids for the Panama Canal, saw the founding of the world-wide success of AGA, using the extraordinary products invented by Gustaf Dalén. This canal project, which was completed in 1913, saw the company manufacturing leading lights and buoys.

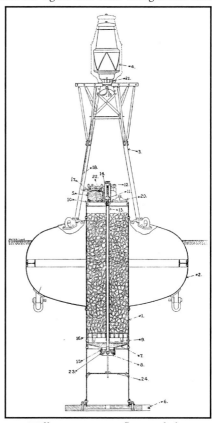

However, acetylene would have a limited life span as a fuel for navigation lights, in the same way, as oil was superseded by electricity. During the 1930's, attempts to employ battery powered equipment in buoys and beacons were made in the USA. Although these systems were ingeniously engineered and well made, they could not equal the reliability of the marine acetylene fuelled equipment, supplied by AGA or PINTSCH of Germany. Yet since the era of supremacy, the acetylene or propane gas methods have slowly been phased out by the introduction of electronics and the advent of solar powered systems.

When used on buoys, acetylene gas did have many advantages. Its lightsource was large, so it was possible to produce a wide vertical divergence, which is an important consideration for a buoy. In service, the flame ignites and extinguishes instantly, whereas an electric powered filament lamp takes a short time to warm up or to cool down.

Willson automatic floating light.
Spitzer Archive

39

In turn the filament makes multiple flashing sequences less practicable and also wastes power.

If making a comparison of the life span of each system, a filament lamp is valued at about 1,000 hours, but an acetylene burner will last for several years. Wherever where mantles were used, they were probe to brakage, which required the introduction of an ingenious mechanism which detected the breakage and changed to a new mantle, placed in focus with the lens. The motive power was spring-driven, being rewound after a long service period – usually once per year.

Early battery operated flashers were electromechanical, with an ingenious motor that used minimal current. This *'gnat-power'* was fed to the motor by a specially constructed battery, designed to provide a very slow rate of discharge and with the least amount of self-discharge. Electrical contacts, featured in many early flashing systems, corroded and wore down during service. The motors revolved at high speeds, with the pivots wearing out and causing various operational problems; but these early flasher systems were innovative products for the period in which they were employed. Although in comparison, the acetylene method had cams, pivots and valves, but was superbly designed and manufactured like a fine clock. The power available to work it was considerable – being derived from the pump at the gas-filling plant by which the gas pressure was provided. This pressure remained sufficient within the gas cylinder at its distant site aboard a buoy or beacon and, with 18psi, gave ample mechanical power to operate the flasher.

During the late 1930's, England and the United States of America had two manufacturers who competed in the development of a special, pure-lead grid, secondary battery. These exceptional devices were produced to supply power for over 12 months, without the need for recharging the batteries. The DP Battery Company (England) and The Willard Battery Company (USA), both succeeded with the production of these secondary battery packs, but neither of their designs took kindly to sea-water contamination. Whereas during this same period, the ever reliable acetylene cylinder-stacks were capable of swilling around in this salty environment for around 30 years without any detriment.

Fog & Rain

Perhaps it was believed by the scientific community of the times, that the high intensity arc lamps, being magnified through the majestic optics, would solve the problems for providing a visual reference for shipping during foggy conditions. But in reality this became a forlorn hope, for one would be unlikely to see even the sun through fog. Yet what the eye could not see, maybe the ear might hear.

For about 80 years various methods were introduced to enable shipping to continue their voyages, either by lightstation to ship, or ship-to-ship audible signals. But the early systems only allowed these vessels to progress at very reduced speeds, which effectively put them in the vulnerable situation of being at the mercy of the currents and tides. With only a compass left for navigation and no landfall to fix a position, the fog became a deadly enemy.

Firstly on-board gongs gave way to bells, then to fog guns and exploding rockets. Then, in America, Brown Brothers of New York developed the reed horn, that was powered by steam. It was later adapted and employed with its power derived from compressed air. Although these systems of fog warning signals were installed extensively around the World, they were not economically viable.

In time the next development saw the introduction of the siren, with the first of its kind being installed in an English lighthouse, at Dungeness, around 1865. This idea of a siren dated back to the end of the 18th century and was due to the inventiveness of Dr. John Robinson (1739-1803). A Frenchman, Charles Cagniard de la Tour, developed the disk unit around 1819 and named it the siren.

Around 1862 Frederick Holmes and George Slight devised their version of the siren, which became widely employed around England. This method consisted of a rotating slotted disc, positioned over a similar fixed perforated plate. Once it had been encased inside a cylinder, compressed air or steam was forced through the unit. Originally these sirens had a distinct character, with the sound gradually rising until the revolving disc was at its optimum speed. It also provided a descending tone as the disc started to slow down. Later versions incorporated a secondary compressed air supply, which spun the rotating disc up to its full speed, prior to the main thrust of air being injected into the cylinder. This method resulted in a very positive and sustainable harmonic note.

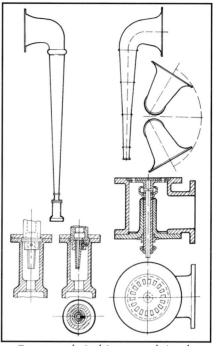

Compressed-air-driven sound signals, reed horn and disk siren.
K. C. Sutton-Jones Collection

Some sirens were developed which utilized a twin cylinder system, often with its inner section having a varied number of slots. This idea produced two different sound frequencies (*high or low*), when the thrust of compressed air activated the siren. However, these first types of devices intended to overcome the background noises aboard ships, which so often masked the sound-signals blast.

To condense and transmit the sounds produced, either by the reed system or the siren, magnificent horns and trumpets were manufactured. They came in several shapes and sizes, with some being flat-sided and tapering outwards from the sound source to nearly 2m (7ft) across its bell mouth. Other horns looked like giant sousaphones with their flaring bells, some of them were laid sideways on to a fog-signal house, as tapering cylindrical units. Examples of this type of horn were installed at Round Island (Isles of Scilly), Alderney and Flatholm in the Bristol Channel.

One of the largest horns manufactured and installed at an English lightstation, was the exceptional horizontal Rayleigh trumpet, which was almost 7.5m (24ft) long. This unit was sited at the Trevose Head station on the north Cornwall coast and recorded as being powerful enough, to vibrate cups and saucers off shelves up to three miles away.

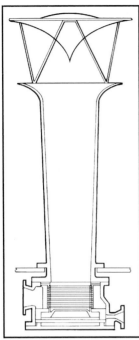

Vertical diaphone for light-ships and isolated lighthouses.
K. C. Sutton-Jones Collection

One of the most awesome compressed air fog-signals was the *'diaphone'*, originally invented around 1903 by Joseph P. Northey, a Canadian. It consisted of a slotted piston and a corresponding perforated cylinder. When the piston was reciprocated within the cylinder by the compressed air, once the air supply was admitted to the slots in the cylinder, it was cut by the reciprocating piston, whereupon it produced an exceptional *'bellowing'* sound, rich in harmonics and audible for several miles. When the air supply was terminated at the end of the blast, it caused the sound to end with a sharply descending and characteristic *'grunt'*. This made it readily distinguishable from other whistles and sounds at sea. Some of these diaphone stations were extremely powerful and had instruments mounted in pairs, blowing together at the same frequency producing the *'gargantuan'* and almost *'seismic'* sensation to anyone in close proximity.

Chance Brothers of Birmingham (England), became one of the main suppliers for this type of fog signal to many lightstations around the World.

An economic compressed air driven signal, known as the *'typhon'*, was invented around 1920 by H. Rydberg of Kokums, Sweden, and produced a higher frequency sound, similar to a ship's whistle.

Electricity was later used to great effect with the development of the *'sound emitter'*, or *'nautophone'*. This devise was invented in Germany in 1926. Its principle operation consisted of a steel membrane, set between the poles of a magnet. As an alternating current of electricity was passed through the insulated copper windings around the magnet, it caused the membrane to vibrate. Its sound frequency was between 300Hz to 500Hz, with an audible range of up to 5 nautical miles. These types of electromagnetic fog-signal emitters were capable of operating in an unattended mode, and they are still widely employed around the World today.

The era of the powerful fog-horns lasted for about 50 years, before bowing out to the *'Racon'*. During the time these *'majestic'* sound systems were in service, such as the *'L or K'* diaphones, they disturbed the keepers and local residents alike. Yet with all this noise, it was surprising how the keepers and their families actually became immune to the nuisance and impediment to a sound-sleep.

The last of these major signals were adapted to produce three different frequencies of sound. In theory the idea was, to enable the mariner to have a number of chances to hear the signal above the extraneous noises on board a ship. Also many of the larger fog-signal systems consumed enormous quantities of fuel and were dependant on thermal pressures and the variations in wind direction, to provide an effective transmission of their signals.

These days the established sound signals do not have that *'earth shattering'* power and simply transmit a *'puny'* high frequency tone as a means to inform a vessel that it

42

must stop or change course, before it collides with an automated lightstation.

Invisible Positioning

A network of 'Radio Direction Fixing Beacons' was introduced from about 1930 onwards, with the method adopted by many countries. The system required various stable sites to be fitted with special radio transmitters. On board a ship was installed a radio receiver, which had a rotating loop aerial. This was gently turned by the operator until the strongest transmission was received. Each of these transmitters had their own call sign, and with the aid of a compass bearing, a line could be drawn on to a navigation chart. By taking the bearings from two or three known beacons, it was possible to assess a fairly accurate position for the vessel where all of the lines crossed.

Another form of *'radio transmitter'* was first used at the Cumbrae station on the Clyde (Scotland), and employed in conjunction with the *'grunt'* of its diaphone during foggy conditions. This method was known as the *'Talking Lighthouse'*. The transmitters work began, when the blast from the diaphone terminated. At this time the radio transmitter was synchronised to broadcast a series of numbers at one second intervals. On board the vessel these numbers would start 1,2,3,4 etc., received almost instantly after transmission. However, on the basis that sound travels at approximately one mile per second, when the external sound of the diaphone reached the vessel, the corresponding number referred to the distance (*in miles*) that it was from the transmitter. This device was not employed extensively around the *'British Isles'*, but it is understood the system did gain a certain degree of credence in North America.

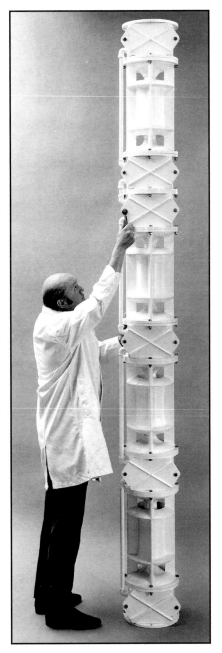

Two-miler stack emitter.
K. C. Sutton-Jones Collection

Above: Triple frequency electric signal at Anvil Point lighthouse, England. Photograph Karl R. Spitzer Left: Sealed beam units at Round Island lighthouse, Isles of Scilly, England. With kind permission of Trinity House. Right: A combination of both at Dungeness lighthouse, England. Photograph Karl R. Spitzer

Morse Code & Semaphore

Communications for keepers on rock-based stations were extremely primitive up to the 1930's. In most cases the same method used to signal ship to ship was employed, such as the morse lamp or semaphore flags. Although there were distress rockets at most of these lighthouses, their usage was strictly for shipping or a dire emergency at the station.

On one occasion during these early days, a principal keeper was taken ill, but not in a life-threatening way. Yet it was necessary for his companions to use the morse lamps to transmit an urgent message to a passing ship. Luckily a relief boat was able to reach the station in question (Eddystone), and to take the keeper back to Plymouth. Following this incident, Trinity House implemented a programme of installing valve operated radio telephones into these isolated stations.

Even with this 'modern' innovation, lightstations such as the Wolf Rock and Longships (to the South-west of Land's End, England), were frequently storm-bound for weeks at a time. On several occasions, prior to the advent of helicopters, small planes dropped emergency supplies onto the lantern gallery. For those involved with the delivery of the provisions, it took the precision skills of an expert 'bomb-aimer' to carry out these missions successfully.

Various Methods of Hyperbolic Positioning

The 'Decca' system offered a service to shipping which were fitted with special receivers. These hyperbolic positioning signals provided either 'Red', 'Green' or 'Purple' references to the vessel and plotted the information on special charts displaying grid lines. In turn these co-ordinates, shown on the receiver, plotted the true geographical location of the ship. The system operated in the 70–130kHz frequency band, normally using groups of three or more transmitter stations, known as a 'chain'. Decca provided a high degree of accuracy by day, yet less at night, even so it was extensively employed.

There is a general trend to change to the hyperbolic system known as 'LORAN-C', which provides a day/night accuracy similar to the Decca and operates in the 90-110kHz frequency range. However, for harbour approach the 'Differential LORAN-C' gives a higher accuracy over a limited area by utilizing UHF.

'RANA' (or RAdio NAvigation) is a further hyperbolic method, that has been employed mostly in fishing areas and is used in a 'chain' system over the whole of the Bay of Biscay (France).

'SYLEDIS' is applicable, where hydrographic surveying and positioning of oil platforms and drilling rigs ect. occur, which require a high degree of accuracy. There are many other systems which are being developed, including Global positioning methods using satellites.

The Full Umbrella 'To Guide Their Way'

In many countries the open sea, coastal aids to navigation, those with estuaries, ports, harbours and rivers, are under separate functioning authorities. There is also another controlling body for those industries connected with mining and oil operations. Our study so far has featured the coastal and open sea methods of 'hazard marking', and wherever practical or economically feasible, these have been lighthouses on a firm foundation such as rocks, or set upon piles, driven into the

»Nore« lightship 1731. Spitzer Archive

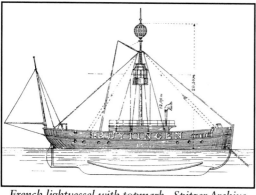

French lightvessel with topmark. Spitzer Archive

sand, gravel or swamp. In the latter cases many of these open-work towers or similar structures, were set upon screw-ended piles, but now they are usually of concrete, forced into the relative section of *'ooze'*.

Where shifting sand or subsea rock, gravel or other banks are a danger to shipping, they have been marked by buoys or moored lightvessels. Some are equipped with a means of self-propulsion, but all of them are moored very securely.

The first lightvessel, or *'lightship'*, was moored at Nore Sand in the Thames estuary (England) around 1731, to assist the guidance of shipping, entering or leaving the Port of London. Other such lightvessels were established around England, but these often broke adrift when the heavy seas snapped their rope lines. With the advent of chains in 1820, most of these problems were overcome. Yet many of these early vessels were extremely primitive, and only converted from their original sailing usage into lightships. During the following years specially designed wooden or composite vessels, of approximately 35m (115ft) length, were brought into service. These ships had a central mast, plus a mizen sail to assist the crew in keeping the vessel *'bow-on'* to the sea. Its main mast carried a lantern, which could be lowered for servicing purposes, and usually a topmark whereby the identity of the station would be noted as the lightvessel rose above the horizon.

Each of these early lightship lanterns contained a lighting apparatus comprising gimbal-mounted parabolic mirrors, with an oil-wick lamp. The assemblies were rotated by a weight-driven clock mechanism, located at the base of the mast, with its power transmitted to the light apparatus above by means of a shaft and a spigot. The intensity of the revolving light was about 12,000 candelas, with its rotations adjustable, according to the set character of the station.

Later it was usual for a vessel to have a compressed air reed or siren, which sounded by means of a spring or weight-driven timing device, that allowed the signal to emit either a high or low alternating blast to aid identification. However, in Calcutta not even a small engine was provided to produce the compressed air; all that was available for these vessels was *'man-power'*.

These vessels normally had a large open day-space below decks, with bed cubicles for the crew and a separate cabin, office and quarters for the Master or Deputy in charge. The romantic tales, devised by numerous writers, lead one to believe that such a life rolling and pitching on the end of a mooring cable in high seas (*but actually travelling nowhere*), was found to be attractive by some people.

After the second World War, Trinity House embarked upon a building programme for lightvessels, which led to a truly superb class of ship, with accommodation, high powered lighting and sound signalling equipment - and eventually the introduction of a helipad, to transfer personnel and provisions by means of a helicopter. Many of these vessels are still in service today, having been converted to un-manned, automated and monitored operation.

Around the same time as England, Sweden, Denmark and the Orient carried out a modernisation programme of their lightships and also set them up as fully manned stations. Although many others have been replaced by lightfloats or automatic buoys.

Lightvessels in Canada and the United States were usually manned and self-propelled, so as to allow the ship to go and return from station. Other vessels were not fitted with engines and had to be towed to and from station. In areas which were prone to hurricanes and cyclones it was important, that a means was readily available to return the vessels to an assigned location as quickly as possible, with the majority of these ships having self-propulsion to achieve this.

Over the past few years lightvessels were equipped with lighting and sound-signalling aids, generally similar as installed in lighthouses and beacons. But in addition a submarine bell, that sounded to an assigned character, was in service on many vessels and provided a distinctive means of determining its location, using the hydrophone on board a ship.

Wigham automatic petroleum lantern.
Spitzer Archive

Estuary and Channel Marking

Over the years numerous aids have been added, to facilitate entry and safe progress within widely variant estuaries, rivers and canals around the World. Many of these early minor beacons were unlit and extremely elementary in their construction. Often they consisted only of a basket, cone, diamond, globe or trapezium shape marker, mounted upon a pole or wooden structure. Similarly buoys were rudimentary rope-moored floats of can, cone spherical or spar shape, according to the channel location and the onward navigable course for the ship. Early methods saw the vessels waiting outside the entrance to this water course, either for daylight or moonlit periods, because of the unsuitable tidal depth, before entering the navigable channel. As these waterways became dredged, it was practicable for vessels to enter or leave according to the tidal flow and its depth, but this necessitated the channel markers to be lit.

Wigham lantern on lighted beacons.
Spitzer Archive

One of the earliest methods of illuminating were wax fuelled lights. These were closely followed by oil. Notably the Wigham oil burning marine lantern, in which the wick was on a roller attached to a float. As the oil in the container was spent, the float pulled the burning part of the wick and eliminated the need to trim the wick manually. These lamps provided an unattended service for up to 90 days before they required replenishment.

In 1881 Nyberg and Lyth provided a major development, with their oil-gas system for beacons and buoys. Its provision of riveted, iron plated buoys performed an unattended and very creditable operation over a period of several days. During the early part of 1882, Linberg introduced a system for beacons, in which an oil wick lamp and chimney were installed inside a Fresnel lens. The heat rising through the chimney exited through a pivoted collection of rotating vanes, that in turn caused the optical screens to rotate around the lamp. The arrangement of the optical panels could be adjusted, to provide a wide range of flashing or occulting characters. Red, green or blanking screens, fitted to its lantern glazing, allowed the apparatus to cater for the numerous displays of coloured sectors so prevalent in Nordic waterways.

Enormous changes in all systems of illumination came in the 1880's, with the invention of the incandescent gas mantle by Dr. Auer von Welsbach. When used

48

with stored, compressed oil-gas or liquid 'Blau-gas', which could be transported in small steel tanks, along with Dr. Julius Pintsch's system of illumination, it formed the next phase in unattended service, both for beacons and buoys. The firm of Pintsch Bamag of Germany is still a highly respected manufacturer and supplier for the needs for navigation today.

As the 20th century began, acetylene gas became a prominent means of fuel. In 1912 Gustav Dalén, the inventor of the system, succeeded in extending its unattended service of a buoy or beacon to over a year, tragically, he lost his eyesight in an accident. Yet this AGA system and its associated equipment has become the 'Hallmark of Excellence' throughout the World.

With larger vessels plying their trade between new ports, it necessitated much dredging and the lengthening of navigable channels. In turn, this brought about world-wide demand for leading marks and lights, beacons and illuminated buoys. Where electricity was available, this was employed to good affect, but often there was an acetylene-powered burner set up, to come into service in the event of power failure.

Up to 50 years ago the 'British' Admiralty List of Lights displayed a 'U' against the name of every unmanned lighted beacon or lighthouse, which implied that it could not be totally relied upon. Cessation of this 'unwarranted' sign heralded the long road towards total unmanning and unattended operation world-wide. Changes in the mode of most lighted aids to navigation would take place, not once, but at least twice and for many reasons.

The Radar Innovation

World War II produced Radar, which, along with the jet engine and television, was invented by British research engineers. The 'smudgy' products of the first seemingly 'miraculous' responses have been refined very much since its inception over 50 years ago. Yet its introduction meant, that a vessel no longer needed to remain anchored in dense fog, nor proceed at dead slow, listening for the 'blare' warning-signal from another ship, lighthouse or lightvessel, because those on watch had 'new eyes' with which to see ahead. As a result, the enormously powerful sound signals became a thing of the past, but in exercising caution, lower powered 'two milers' were produced, to protect both the light station and ship from collision.

Radar responses vary, with some land masses giving a clear 'echo', whilst low lying estuaries do not. For this reason it was necessary to have the hazards marked by lighthouses, beacons or buoys, in order to provide additional clarity to the response. Originally mechanical, angular radar reflectors were employed. The more important locations from a navigational angle were equipped

The racon: 'a most valuable aid to navigation'.
K. C. Sutton-Jones Collection

49

with *'Racons'*, which return the incident probe from a ship's radar back to the observer, in the form of a morse-coded display on the *'scope'*, known as a *'plan-posi-tion-indicator'*.

Although there is a danger that too many displays of 'morse-responses' could be confusing. Accordingly a very useful *'R.T.E.'* (*Radar Target Enhancer*) has been introduced, which highlights the normal 'bright dot' response from a buoy or beacon carrying such a device.

Truly amazing developments are being introduced, among which are *'electronic charts'*, *'identity responders'* aboard vessels and *'radar surveillance'* of ships under passage. There is also the general instant communication system between vessels and the head office or harbour control, which is all part of the *'vessel-traffic-services'* or V.T.S. This dashes the notions cherished by a ship's Master of being *'Master Under God'* aboard his Vessel. Compliance to meet prearranged arrival times for an allotted berth, along with the economic pressure to *'slot'* the turn around time in port to suit the services ashore and management targets, make sea going so competitive and coercive.

Crises – Firstly Oil, then Keepership Threatened

The world-wide notion that oil reserves were at risk and had to be conserved, alerted us all to find ways of cherishing fuel availability. There was also the need for introducing alternative economical ways of empowering aids to navigation, by reducing the expensive transference of diesel and other fuels over sea or land to the various lightstations.

Following the exceptional project undertaken by Gellerstad in Sweden, that resulted in the replacement of light-vessels by submergible concrete towers, it was decided to implement a programme of complete automation.

In the shallow Baltic Sea it became practicable to transfer mains electrical power by underwater cables to out-stations. This method, together with the innovative programme initiated by Lennart Hallengren, introduced the World's lighthouse *'Chiefs'* as to the viability and practical sense of conveying stores and personnel by helicopter.

Access by helicopter even in wild conditions had been proven, with one exception being during thick fog. Lightstations could now be automated using acetylene gas equipment, and even in the rare event of its failure, it was possible for a technician to be flown out without the delays of a sea landing. The demise of the regular attendance by light-keepers appeared ominously on the horizon, and the unmanning of major offshore stations loomed as a real spectre.

Economic Recession

Reductions in the various fleets of tenders, carrying crews on relief and technicians, became inevitable. Drastic measures aboard ship to economise, in order to keep afloat during this recession, became essential. Shipping companies and other users of aids to navigation had long complained that the light dues were an excessive burden.

Under the stress of recession it became impractical, and sometimes unreasonable, to expect large vessels to pay very high light dues at the end of a voyage. This was particularly relevant as few of the traditional aids could be seen during a voyage, especially for a ship employing a track far from the normal coastal approach.

Those lightstations within coastal waters were used by smaller vessels, many of which paid little or nothing towards the cost of the upkeep, for what was a very elaborate, yet safe and reliable service.

Shippings Revised Requirements

The shipping industry in general complained, that recent advances in navigation practice made a comprehensive and complex service totally unnecessary. Such over-elaboration came about to some extent, because of the electrification of apparatus originally constructed for use with oil burners. Whereas these systems were originally designed to produce a light of some 300,000 candelas, the introduction of a high-luminance, electrical light-source caused beams of millions of candelas to sweep the horizon in spectacular fashion. This was considered at the time as *'jolly good'*, but such a surfeit of power, produced at an increased cost, could not contribute any real benefit.

The economics in operating and maintaining a service, in which the cost for isolated lighthouses, lightvessels and buoys, together with land-based stations are high, was particularly noticeable where many had two crews (*service and on leave*), and required transfers either by helicopter or ship. Adding to this the additional staffing at fog signal stations, plus the logistics in the deployment of facilities, the cost was very high indeed.

Several countries, proud that all was free to the user, obviously had to reconsider the high expenditure, especially as it was borne by the tax payer. Yet while the Swedish Lighthouse Service had managed to reduce its total staffing to some 200 personnel, other authorities, having a comparable number of navigation aids, were employing up to ten times the complement of people.

Unmanning Major Lightstations

Gustaf Dalén's automatic lighthouse, working from acetylene gas, could provide an effective intensity of just over 100,000 candelas. But this was not enough to accommodate the requirements of a large container ship, making 20 knots, that needed to see a major light from 22-24 nautical miles away. Local mains electricity could be employed, with a standby power generation plant in the event of failure. For isolated rock, or light-vessel stations in wild seas, the need for a reliable source of generated power was paramount, and this was achieved by specially adjusting the components in a diesel-fuelled engine. This method was employed in the unmanning and automation of the Eddystone (England) in 1982, just 100 years after its construction. The system supplied all the services, including an electric fog-signal, and was very elaborately and successfully engineered under the direction of Ian Clingan OBE, the

Eddystone remote control unit at Penlee.
K. C. Sutton-Jones Collection

Above: Sevenstones lightvessel, UK. Photograph Chris Foulds · Below: Display of different optics at the Shore Village Museum, Rockland, Maine, USA. Photograph Karl R. Spitzer

Engineer-in-Chief at that time. The station was then monitored by VHF radio from a shore station at Penlee Point, to the west of Plymouth (England). By the end of 1998 the entire lighthouse services in the United Kingdom and Eire will have been completely automated and monitored from a centralised control centre.

Initially the economical *'pruning'* process required a new type of lighting apparatus, which was a powerful system employing rotating panels of sealed beam lamps, as installed at Dungeness (England), rather than to invest in the very costly ground and polished glass optical assembly. Yet it still uses energy in kilowatts and is dependant upon the availability of suitable lamps, similar to the types used in road and rail transportation. Some lighted aids employ even more highly developed lamps, small in size of source, yet providing a great brilliance. However, this has bedevilled the suppliers of lighthouse equipment, ever since electricity took over from gas and oil, simply because the quantities being required are small in comparison. Therefore it is not an economical consideration for the lampmakers for these types of light-source, especially with the lifetime of employment for each unit being extended from the original 1,000 hours of service.

High powered lights are a necessity where position fixing is needed on a point in front of an intensely illuminated area, such as oil flares near refineries, or lighted walls of high rise buildings, particularly when reflected in a waterfront like Singapore.

Conserving Energy

Economising on costs became accepted as a world-wide necessity, with the diesel engine being tuned to provide a continuous unattended service for many months between servicing. The visits by the technical staff could be spread to twice, or three times a year. But it still required fuel, normally delivered annually to an unmanned station either by ship, helicopter, or overland by trucks. Yet the former exceptional cleanliness and *'sparkle'* of an isolated tower-rock lighthouse in the keepership days, when an optic received a daily clean, could not be maintained; especially with a diesel engine atmosphere.

A British Government department developed a thermal-electric generator, in which a propane gas burner was used to heat one end of a diaphragm-mounted container, filled with helium. This caused the unit to oscillate vertically, and thereby energised a battery-charging circuit, from which an isolated lighthouse could receive a highly efficient conversion of power. But certain mechanical difficulties were encountered while in service, which brought about its withdrawal. Drums containing propane gas had to be delivered, although, as in the case of acetylene cylinders and emergency diesel fuel, they were transported to site underslung by helicopter.

Experimental work has striven long and hard to convert the power of sea-waves into a usable source for producing electrical power. Success was achieved in Japan by harnessing the rise and fall of a buoy in the water, that pumped a column of air through a turbine connected to a generator. Yet so much depended upon wave height, periodicity, weight and the size of the buoy for maximising the results. But this method was brought into service successfully in many countries. Another system for harnessing the power of tidal variation has been considered for the production of electricity, but it is not known by the Author whether any of this development was intended for lighthouse illumination.

Nuclear reaction was in service in many lightstations, particularly in countries formerly allied to Russia. It was also utilized in Ireland at the Rathlin O'Birne station, although this has now been superseded. In any case nuclear systems would be very expensive, especially for the specialist technicians (*presuming them to be willing to work on such projects*), to service such reactors, and it is this which limits employment of such hazardous equipment.

The Great Panacea

Power from the sun is a source that affects all of our lives, yet we have been digging up mines to obtain coal for fuel or drilling holes to extract oil. So much of the sun's energy has been wasted, simply because there was not a means to utilize this mighty potential. It has only been during the comparatively recent years, that a suitable method of employing this natural resource became available, along with the means to deliver its power in a readily usable form.

It is over 20 years since the Author was first involved in the testing of solar energy, as a means to power marine navigational aids. But it is true to say that this form of energy is now universally employed. Its success has not been attributable entirely to the provision of solar converter modules or panels, but to the fact that the conversion of the sun's energy along with reliable electronic components arrived concurrently, with a profound influence for both the user and the supplier.

The micro-chip and the subsequent invasion of its use by the world of electronics, has transformed the solar power available into a converted form and ready for use for maintaining the charging of a battery. These systems are usually on top of a buoy structure and clear of the sea. This method has all but eclipsed the acetylene and propane gas equipment and revolutionised the structure, plus the manufacturing complexities of most companies engaged in this highly specialist field.

Chance Brothers - lighhouse fitting shop.
K. C. Sutton-Jones Collection

The Author's mind reflects upon the manufacturing companies who made the whole equipment and built many of the towers needed in the Colonial days. Because of the volume of prisms demanded in an optic constructed during the oil-wick burner times, it could be said that the lighthouse industry was founded upon glass and the Chance *'Glassus'* as it was known, with its workforce of over a thousand operatives. Among numerous items it produced the prismatic mouldings to the *'Lightus'* (*lighthouse works*) alongside, which employed a further 400 people in its heyday. Towers in cast iron, enormous lanterns containing optics rotating on mercury and revolved by clockwork mechanisms, also with burners all fabricated departmentally, were made in-house: This system was later extended to embrace the special switch-gear and engine generator plants, demanded in the electrification phase. Fog horns, also with their majestic compressor machinery, were in another department of this former truly magnificent factory. But the failure to adapt to the changes or to grow with the times, swept all of it away.

Today the optic enclosing its very bright light-source is usually a unit one cubic metre in size and needs no lantern-house, unless it is in a position where the sheltered servicing of the unit in situ is required. Lenses are produced by specialist companies from moulded plastic, with very little machining of the die cast metal components being required, when compared to the precision skills needed for the former gas flashers or pedestal turntables. Buoys and tower structures formerly of steel plate, are often formed from modular plastic or aluminium.

Solar arrays, radio control and other equipment is so expert and specialised, that it is no wonder that instead of the '*Mighty Four Companies*' being in this field of business, there are perhaps over one hundred participants. Designing assembly, testing, installation and servicing is still where the knowledge and experience counts, as to what will, or will not operate in the variety of marine environments from the Poles to the Tropics.

Global Positioning

Positioning satellites in space has revolutionised the tasks of a navigating officer at sea or in the air. Differential Global Positioning systems, when properly installed, dispense with the need for a '*running fix*' on coastal stations and effectively provides a means of obtaining a location accuracy to within a 20 metre diameter circle. So avidly has this '*boom*' to navigation been taken up, even by the small craft user, that many might wonder whether lighthouses will be required at all in the next millennium. However equipment aboard ship or a small boat could fail, whereas the recognised aids to navigation in most countries are maintained to an extremely high standard of reliability and performance. Certainly a hazard ahead is best marked whatever the sophistication of the various pieces of equipment on board a vessel, but there is a case for decommissioning many coastal '*fixing*' stations. Also estuaries and channels where under keel depths are vital, still require very conspicuous marking and to be illuminated.

For the positioning of buoys they not only need to be secure, but monitored and this is where the D.G.P.S. plays a major role. Any deviation of a buoy from its watch circle can be detected, with the information immediately being transmitted to a Port Control Officer, who can speedily implement the necessary repositioning.

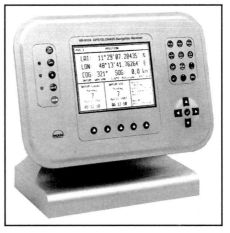

GPS/GLONASS - Global positioning shipboard receiver. K. C. Sutton-Jones Collection

For the lighting of buoys in particular, but beacons also, the *'flavour'* for the LED (*Light Emitting Diode*) is gaining ground as a logical and suitable source of light.

Refinement of the Monitoring

A process of monitoring the operation of a distant station has been available for many years, in the form of coast watchers and keepers who reported upon the status of neighbouring lights. Early types of automatic radio transmitting devices fitted as part of the lighting apparatus, were considered less reliable than the equipment they monitored, much to the amazement of technicians sent to a station to *'correct'* faults. On numerous occasions it was found that a problem did not exist with the lighting apparatus, but only with the monitoring transmitters.

Following the Swedish experience of initiating servicing needs by noting the display on a central monitoring screen, it was found to be a cost saver and comforting proof that the stations were in operation as they should be. This method caught on and has been adopted widely throughout many National Services. The positioning or monitoring of light-vessels and buoys is a refinement being pursued in many Lighthouse and Port Administrations, but it adds to the complexity of the equipment being employed. For short range monitoring VHF is the common medium, with UHF utilized in exceptional circumstances. But for distant monitoring the *'Meteor-Burst Communication System'* is in service along with transmissions via satellites. Once polled by a base station transmitter the out station reports the operational status of selected vital components.

The Pruning Process

In the true meaning of the word to *'prune'* or 'be rid of dead or overgrown parts', seems to be the apt description that was readily adopted in the downgrading of many navigation lights. The luxuriant shore station of the past on its gale swept promontory, complete with somewhat *'Spartan'* quarters for three or four keepers and their families (*if accessible schooling facilities were available for the children*), was indeed impressive to the cliff walking visitor evoking romantic overtones in his mind. This station, complete with its million candela powered landfall light and thunderous fog horn, would occupy several acres of ground, be complete with a private roadway, track or sea-landing, to enable fuel to be supplied and provide relieving facilities for keepers and personnel.

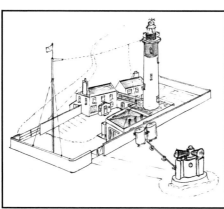

Yesterday's major station.
K. C. Sutton-Jones

In addition the boundary wall enclosed gardens where the keepers could grow vegetables. Suitable storage space was provided for fuel, with the large receivers for the compressed air driven fog signal very conspicuous, as were the black trumpets that had to be avoided in case the loud *'booming'* units suddenly *'burst'* into life.

A down graded version needed only the tower, now unnecessarily massive, for containing the small modern light apparatus that provided just half the original intensity of the original system, yet adequate in the new D.G.P.S. navigation era. An array of solar panels charged the battery that operated the lighting unit, small sound signal (*if off-shore rocks dictated that vessels should stop in fog*), with the out-station radio monitoring equipment being mounted on the lantern gallery or its roof.

Only a small billet was now required to accommodate visiting technicians, with all the remaining buildings being surplus to the needs of this modernised lighthouse. To demolish them would save the heavy costs of maintenance, yet alternatively such prime sites could encourage thoughts of turning these buildings into suitable holiday accommodation.

Realistically, the essential ingredients of its modern equivalent would be modest by comparison with its predecessor. Its light unit would be on top of a 15m (49ft) high tower, comprising mouldings of glass reinforced plastic bolted together. All the equipment for operating the light could be kept in secure conditions inside the tower. Solar energy panels would adorn the structure, raised above the light, which also powered the Racon. Any sound system, together with its back-scatter, infra-red fre-

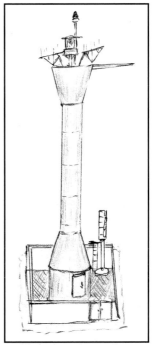

Today's major station.
K. C. Sutton-Jones

quency fog detector would be sited at ground level beside the structure, or positioned on the roof of the small accommodation cabin utilized by the visiting technician. The whole complex would then be enclosed behind a solid boundary wall, complete with its anti-intruder security fence on top. The entire plot of land for this new station need measure no more than 100 m², with a road to the site not essential because no fuel had to be delivered.

Yet a tower rock lighthouse indicates a hazard to shipping and its complexion would not change, for it has to withstand extreme sea and weather conditions. Most of the modern equipment would be inside its lantern, with the helipad providing easy access for service personnel. But it is probably true to say that the *'romantic notion'* in the public perception of a lighthouse on its rock will be preserved, without a doubt, it would be costly to remove it. Now there will no longer be the towel-waving keeper to acknowledge a ship's flag salute – he has most likely *'swallowed the anchor'* and pulled away from life at sea some years ago. Maybe he now lives in retirement in Bradford, or on the *'Costa Brava'* in Spain.

Meanwhile the navigating officers aboard a container ship or mammoth oil-carrying tanker, or maybe their counterparts in the cabins of yachts and fishing boats, are bouncing interrogation probes off satellites, in the belief that they know exactly where the vessel is located, without the *'trinkets'* or the skills of the former *'lighthouse engineer'*.

This may change when approaching a harbour or silting estuary, for then these mariners will still prefer to use their eyes along with the radar. Therefore the probability is, that aids to navigation at the beginning or end of a voyage will receive intensifying attention, make them more conspicuous, brighter, efficient and safer to use, in the knowledge that their performance and accurate positioning will be constantly monitored. Yet courage could be developed by the mariner, so that it be possible to sail along blindly and only looking at a scope. However, the Author does not believe this will happen, because ships have awfully poor brakes.

Participants of the 1950 Lighthouse Conference in Paris. K. C. Sutton-Jones Collec-

The International Forum

In 1957 the International Association of Lighthouse Authorities (IALA) was formed, through the enthusiastic work of the close association of its founder motivators, Paul Petry (France), P.J.G. van Diggelen (The Netherlands), Sir Gerald Curteis of Trinity House (England) and Gerhard Wiedemann (Germany).

Prior to this establishment of the International forum, conferences were held at certain National Lighthouse Services headquarters, or similar venues, to which observers from invited specialists of noted manufacturers of lighthouse apparatus and equipment could attend. The first of these conference-style meetings was instigated by the Prince of Wales (*later to become Edward VII of England*) around 1895. These conferences continued on a regular basis and were only interrupted by the first and second World Wars. The Author attended the Paris Conference that was held in 1950, the first since the end of hostilities.

In addition to structures, buoys and the management of them, the subjects discussed related to the uniform establishment of International standards for navigation safety. At the 1975 IALA conference (Canada), Capt. Bury (*the Warden of Trinity House*), emphasized that there were some 30 systems of buoy-marking in the World, declaring "*Gentleman, it is in a mess!*". Accordingly he and Norman Matthews, the former Secretary-General of IALA/AISM, drew up a system of marking which secured international acceptance at the next 1980 conference (Japan). This system has proved to be highly acceptable and demonstrated the effectiveness of IALA as an instrument of maritime safety.

Today, with the emphasis on automation, radio, radar, hyperbolic positioning aids, electronics, monitoring and alternative power systems, the quest for improvements in efficiency, reliability and the economy of operation has dramatically changed. There are now over 77 National members from various countries, 59 industrial, and 40 honorary members, of which the Author is one such participant. Every four years the IALA holds a special conference with an exhibition staged at a nominated venue.

See It in a Museum

Perhaps behind the awe-inspiring lighthouse you knew little about the magnificence within, yet the skills and the proud maintenance by their keepers were a glory to behold.

There was a time, when refurbishment at a lonely island site involved the casting of the former, majestic optical apparatus and its associated equipment over the edge of a cliff into the sea below, just because it would have been prohibitively costly to transport the items thousands of miles back to habitation. Yet the Northern Lighthouse Board has preserved some of its *'jewels of the past'* within a most enthralling museum at Kinnaird Head, Fraserburgh in Scotland. Trinity House has also established its National Lighthouse Centre at Penzance, where artefacts of a bygone era can still be viewed in all their splendour.

Many services in the USA and Canada have set up similar venues, with Harbour Boards establishing smaller maritime museums, that are open to display these treasures of the past.

Food for Thought

'To Safely Guide Their Way' started with sailors navigating by observing the stars. They now bounce probes off man-installed stars. So are all the lighthouses and equipment to be regarded as just *'so much bric-a-brac'* across the centuries?

Whatever we may feel about the tide of change, the mighty power of the seas must never be taken for granted. For time will never calm this part of our World, which is better expressed in Psalm 107.

'Others went out on the sea in ships, they were merchants on the mighty waters. They saw the works of the Lord, his wonderful deeds in the deep. For he spoke and stirred up a tempest, that lifted high the waves. They mounted up to the heavens and went down to the depths, in their peril their courage melted away. They reeled and staggered like drunken men, they were at their wits end. They cried out to the Lord in their trouble, and he brought them out of their distress. He stilled the storm to a whisper, the waves of the sea were hushed. They were glad when it grew calm, and he guided them to their desired haven.'

Hanois lighthouse
With kind permission of Trinity House

The author expresses his special thanks to Pharos Marine Ltd. for its support and assistance with this publication.

PHAROS MARINE Ltd.
High Street · Brentford · Middlesex · TW8 0AP · Tel. (+44) (0181) 568879

This company welcomes enquiries from the Lighthouse enthusiasts.
They are more than willing to pass any comments or communications to Kenneth Sutton-Jones.

To obtain a special copy of »PHAROS • The Lighthouse - Yesterday, Today and Tomorrow«
by Kenneth Sutton-Jones, write to the above address for further details. A book not to be missed.
This company is also one of the leading manufacturers of maritime aids
and relative equipment around the World.

ASSOCIATION INTERNATIONALE de SIGNALISATION MARITIME
INTERNATIONAL ASSOCIATION of LIGHTHOUSE AUTHORITIES
List of National Members

ALGERIA	Directeur de l'Office National de Signalisation Maritime	ALGER-GARE
ARGENTINA	Jefe · Departamento Seguridad Nautica · Armada Argentina · Servicio Hidrografia Naval	BUENOS AIRES
AUSTRALIA	Chief Executive · Australian Maritime Safety Authority	BELCONNEN · ACT 2681
BARBADOS	The Port Manager · Barbados Port Authority	BRIDGETOWN
BELGIUM	Administration des Affaires Maritimes et de la Navigation	BRUXELLES
BENIN	M. le Directeur du Port Autonome de Cotonou	COTONOU
BERMUDA	Department of Marine and Port Services	HAMILTON
BRAZIL	Centro de Signalização · Diretoria de Hidrografia e Navegação	RIO DE JANEIRO
CAMEROON	M. le Directeur Général de l'Office National des Ports du Cameroun	DOUALA
CANADA	Regional Director · Canadian Coast Guard · Maritime Region	DARTMOUTH · NOVA SCOTIA
CHILE	Marine Signalling Service	VALPARAISO
CHINA	The Director · Marine Safety Administation · Ministry of Communications	BEIJING
COTE D'IVOIRE	Chef de la Division des Phares et Balises du Port Autonome d'Abidjan	ABIDJAN
CROATIA	Plovput Split	SPLIT
CUBA	Dirección de Hidrografia y Geodesia del MINFAR	CIUDAD DE LA HABANA
CYPRUS	The General Manager · Cyprus Ports Authority	NICOSIA
DENMARK	Farvandsvaesenet	KOBENHAVN
ECUADOR	Instituto Oceanografico de la Armada	GUAYAQUIL
EGYPT	Head Central Administration for Lighthouse & Navigation Aid & Maritime Affairs	ALEXANDRIA
ENGLAND & WALES	Deputy Master of Trinity House	LONDON
EQUATORIAL GUINEA	Senales Maritimas de Puertos de Guinea Equatorial	MALABO
ESTONIA	Estonian National Maritime Board	TALLINN
FINLAND	Merenkulkuhallitus	HELSINKI
FRANCE	Administrateur Général des Affaires Maritimes · Sous-Direction des la Navigation Maritime	PARIS
THE GAMBIA	The Managing Director · Gambia Ports Authority	BANJUL
GERMANY	The Director, Maritime Aids to Navigation · Ministry of Transport (Bundesvekehrsministerium)	BONN
GHANA	The Director General · Ghana Ports and Harbours Authority	TEMA
GREECE	Director of Lighthouse Service · Hellenic Navy	PIRAEUS
HAITI	Service Maritime et de Navigation d'Haiti (SEMANAH)	PORT AU PRINCE
HONG KONG	The Director of Marine · Marine Department · Aids to Navigation Section	KWAI CHUNG N.T.
ICELAND	Icelandic Marine Administration	KOPAVOGUR
INDIA	Director General of Lighthouses and Lightships	NEW DELHI
INDONESIA	Direktorat Jenderal Perhubungan Laut	JAKARTA
IRAN	Deputy Managing Director · Ports and Shipping Organization	TEHERAN
IRELAND	Chief Executive · Commissioners of Irish Lights	DUBLIN
ISRAEL	Department of Shipping and Ports · Ministry of Transport	HAIFA
ITALY	Ispettorato dei Fari e del Segnalamento Marittimo	ROMA
JAMAICA	The General Manager · Port Authority of Jamaica	KINGSTON
JAPAN	The Commandant · Maritime Safety Agency	TOKYO
KENYA	The Managing Director · Kenya Ports Authority	MOMBASA

KOREA (DPR)	The Waterways and Lighthouses Division	PYONGYANG
KOREA (Rep.)	Ministry of Maritime Affairs & Fisheries (MOMAF)	SEOUL
KUWAIT	Gen. Administration of Transport Sector · Ministry of Communications	SAFAT
LATVIA	Latvian Hydrographic Service	RIGA
MACAU	Capitão dos Portos	MACAU
MALAYSIA	The Chairman · Light Dues Board Peninsular Malaysia	PORT KLANG
MEXICO	Director General de Marina Mercante	MUNICIPIO (Libre No. 377)
MOROCCO	Directeur des Ports · Ministère des Travaux Publics	RABAT
MOZAMBIQUE	National Institute of Hydrography and Navigation (INAHINA)	MAPUTO
NETHERLANDS	Directoraat General Scheepvaart en Maritieme Zaken	RIJSWIJK
NEW ZEALAND	The Director of Maritime Safety · New Zealand Maritime Safety Authority	WELLINGTON
NIGERIA	The General Manager · Nigerian Ports Authority	LAGOS
NORWAY	Kustdirektoratet	OSLO
OMAN	Directorate General of Ports and Public Transport · Ministry of Communications	MUSCAT
PAKISTAN	Chief Nautical Surveyor · Ministry of Communications · Ports and Shipping Wing	KARACHI
PANAMA	Sr. Director General · Autorida Portuaria Nacional	PANAMA
PAPUA-NEW GUINEA	Superintendant of Navaids · Maritime Safety Branch · Department of Transport	KONEDOBU
PERU	Director de Hidrografia y Navegacion · Marina de Guerra del Peru	CHUCUITO
PHILIPPINES	The Commandant · Phillipines Coast Guard	MANILA
POLAND	Director of Aids to Navigation · Maritime Office Gdynia	GDYNIA
PORTUGAL	Direcção de Farois	OEIRAS
ROMANIA	Captain de Rangul · Directia Hidrografica Maritima	CONSTANTZA
RUSSIA	The Director · Principal Department of Navigation and Oceanography	SAINT PETERSBOURG
SAUDI ARABIA	Dept. of LMC · Saudi Port Authority	RIYADH
SCOTLAND	General Manager · Northern Lighthouse Board	EDINBURGH
SENEGAL	M. le Directeur du Ports Autonome de Dakar · Chef du Service de Sécurité Maritime	DAKAR
SINGAPORE	Hydrographic Department · Maritime and Port Authority of Singapore	SINGAPORE
SOUTH AFRICA	PORTNET Lighthouse Service	BRAAMFONTEIN
SPAIN	Dpto. Técnico de Señalización Maritima · Puertos del Estado	MADRID
SUDAN	General Manager · Sea Ports Corporation	PORT SUDAN
SWEDEN	Sjöfartsverkets Centralförvaltning	NORRKÖPING
TAIWAN	College of Maritime Science · Ocean University	KEELUNG
TANZANIA	Chief Marine Officer · Tanzania Harbours Authority	DAR ES SALAM
THAILAND	The Director · Hydrographic Department · Royal Thai Navy	BANGKOK
TUNISIA	M. le Chef du Service des Phares et Balises · Ministère de la Défense Nationale	TUNIS
TURKEY	The General Manager · Türkiye Denizcilik Isletmeleri	ISTANBUL
UKRAINE	Director · Mayachna Sluzba	ODESSA
UNITED KINGDOM	Shipping Policy Division · Department of Transport	LONDON
UNITED STATES OF AMERICA	The Commandant · The U.S. Coast Guard	WASHINGTON D.C.
URUGUAY	Jefe del Servicio de Oceanografia · Hidrografia y Meteorologica de la Armada	MONTEVIDEO
VENEZUELA	Oficina Coordinadora de Hidrografia y Navegacion (OCHINA)	MAIQUETIA
VIET NAM	Vietnam Maritime Safety Agency (VMS)	HAIPHONG
YEMEN	The Port Officer and Director of Marine Affairs · Yemen Port Authority	ADEN

INTERNATIONAL GAZETTEER

ASSOCIATION OF LIGHTHOUSE KEEPERS
The Secretary · 2 Queen's Cottages · Queen's Road · Lydd · Kent · TN29 9ND
Formed in 1988 by a group of serving and retired keepers.
Open to membership for all enthusiasts.

BALMORAL MARINE LTD
Balmoral Park · Loirston · Aberdeen AB12 3GY · Scotland · Tel. +44 1224 859200 · Fax +44 1224 859150 · E-mail: marine@balmoral.co.uk
Balmoral Marine Equipment Hire · Balmoral Lloyds Testing · Balmoral Wire Rope Services · Balmoral Nav-Aids

INTERNATIONAL ASSOCIATION OF LIGHTHOUSE AUTHORITIES (IALA)
c/o Paul Ridgeway · 3 The Green · Ketton · Stamford · Lincolnshire · PE9 3RA
Tel. (+44) (01780) 721628 · Fax (+44) (01780) 721980
Specialist contact for information of all the Lighthouse Authorities
and Industrial members around the World.

LEADING LIGHTS MAGAZINE
Peter Williams Associates · c/o Haven Lightship · Milford Marina · Milford Haven · SA73 3AF
Tel (+44) (01646) 698055/698825
Now established as the International Lighthouse Journal.

STICHTING HISTORIE DER KUSTVERLICHTING
Kemphaanstraat 42 · 1701 WS · Den Helder · Netherlands

The aims of the foundation are collecting and maintaining lighthouse and lightship related material.

SWEDEN'S LIGHTHOUSE SOCIETY
c/o Esbjörn Hillberg · Hus 154 · S–43082 Donsö · Sweden
Tel. (+46) (0) 31–972148 · Fax (+46) (0) 31–970623
Founded October 1996 by E. Hillberg of Donsö. Constantly growing membership. All enquiries welcome.

 German Lighthouse Enthusiasts Magazine

c/o Klaus Kern · Pestalozzistrasse 28 · D–65428 Rüsselsheim · Germany · Tel. (+49) (06142) 81607
News of lighthouses, lightships and other seamarks. Plus book reviews, postage stamps and postcards.

U.S. LIGHTHOUSE SOCIETY
c/o Wayne Wheeler · 244 Kearny Street · 5th Floor
San Francisco · CA 94108 · USA · Tel. (+1) 415 - 362 - 7255 · Fax (+1) 415 - 362 - 7464
America's most successful Lighthouse Society was founded in 1984 and has now over 10,000 members.

LIGHTHOUSE DIGEST
P.O. Box 1690 · Wells · Maine 04090 · USA · Tel. (+1) 207 - 646 - 0515 · Fax (+1) 207 - 646 - 0516
The World's only full-colour, monthly magazine, covering American and international lighthouses.

To obtain a free list of 'LIGHTHOUSES OF ENGLAND AND WALES' booklets and the details of our 'NO OBLIGATION TO BUY' bookclub, send a S.A.E. to B&T PUBLICATIONS, 10 Orchard Way, Highfield, Southampton, S017 1RD, U.K. Accounts & Customer Enquiries · Telephone/Fax +44 (0) 1703 366154.

To accompany this collection of 'LIGHTHOUSES OF ENGLAND AND WALES', the author has compiled two special publications. The first booklet is titled: 'LIGHTHOUSES: FOUR COUNTRIES – ONE AIM' and gives an easy to read insight into the Corporation of Trinity House, the Commissioners of Irish Lights, the Commissioners of Northern Lights, Private Lighthouse owners, Royal Letter-Patents and the services which are provided today. This booklet also gives an account of the designers and builders of the lighthouses around the coasts of the British Isles.

The second publication provides a detailed account of the various light-sources, fuels, reflectors and optical apparatus, lanterns and fog warning sytems and an insight into the lives of the designers and manufacturers who supplied these items. Titled: 'LIGHTHOUSES: TO LIGHT THEIR WAY', this booklet has been produced with many archive photos and pictorials, which have been provided by the various Lighthouse Authorities and by the author of 'PHAROS: THE LIGHTHOUSE YESTERDAY, TODAY AND TOMORROW', Kenneth Sutton-Jones. This author has also assisted in a major way, by ensuring that the relative technical details are correct. His help has been greatly appreciated by the author. Each of these booklets can be obtained from bookshops or direct from the publisher, (POST FREE IN UK).

Also available from B&T PUBLICATIONS:

»THE SPITZER COLLECTION« – numerous drawings of lighthouses,
lightvessels, lanterns and optics by H.-G. Spitzer.

Why not join the PHAROS PEN PAL CLUB?
Details from the Secretary:
Ian Beevis · 13 Chyngton Way · Seaford · East Sussex · BN25 4JB · U.K.

Also available in this series are the following publications:

NEEDLES POINT	PORTLAND BILL
LIGHTHOUSES — FOUR COUNTRIES – ONE AIM	
LIGHTHOUSES ——— TO LIGHT THEIR WAY	
EDDYSTONE	BISHOP ROCK
LONGSHIPS	SKERRIES ROCK
KINNAIRD HEAD	SMALLS

Cover design, scanning and typesetting by
HANS-GÜNTER SPITZER
c/o B&T Publications · Orchard Way · Highfield
Southampton SO17 1RD · UK